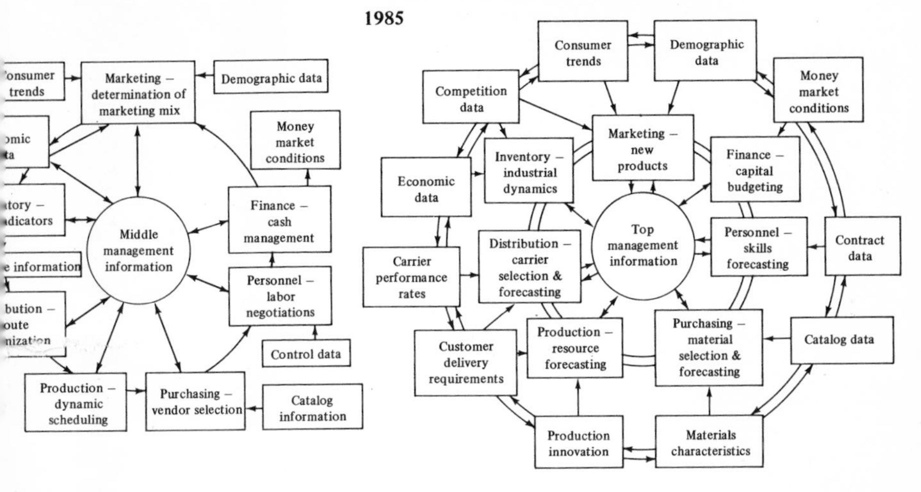

mid-1970's, computer systems will no longer be a management tool for accomplishing the functions zed today as the basics of business. Corporate success determined by the effectiveness of computer applica- t all levels and in all areas of business activity. tial progress will have been made in tapping external r analysis in business decision making. The computer used for tactical planning purposes in many key areas.

The mid-1980's will see a totally new kind of business structure centered on information processing in which internal and external data interact with each other in countless variations. The information system will then be the heart of the structure. All levels of management will be involved in one or another information processing activity. Companies will be information service centers whose highly automated plants will be making this or that product, performing this or that service – all dependent on a total corporate planning system.

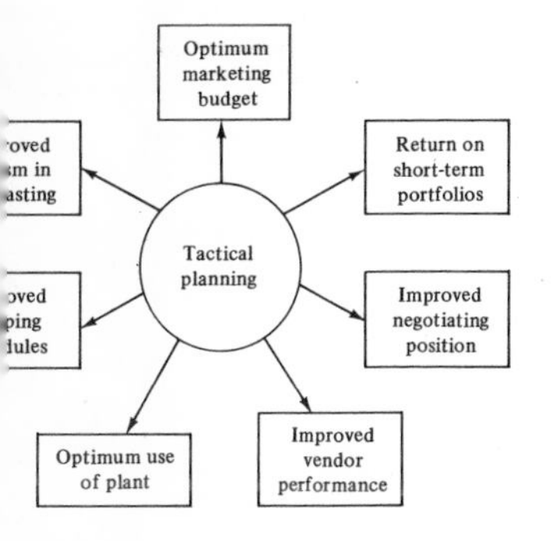

The Diebold Research Program

BUSINESS DECISIONS AND TECHNOLOGICAL CHANGE

BUSINESS DECISIONS AND TECHNOLOGICAL CHANGE

JOHN DIEBOLD

PRAEGER PUBLISHERS
New York · Washington · London

PRAEGER PUBLISHERS
111 Fourth Avenue, New York, N.Y. 10003, U.S.A.
5, Cromwell Place, London S.W.7, England

Published in the United States of America in 1970
by Praeger Publishers, Inc.

Library of Congress Catalog Card Number: 70-95670

Printed in the United States of America

To Ralph Weindling, whose rare gifts and friendship
have made so much possible.

CONTENTS

EXHIBITS

"The social change brought about as a result of technological innovation opens to business its greatest opportunities—and poses the greatest of threats. Machines have always been important to us as agents of social change. The greatest success stories, and the worst tragedies, in business history relate to the ability of businessmen to perceive the meanings of the technological change going on about them and the opportunities they present. This is more true today than ever before."—JOHN DIEBOLD

A NOTE BY THE PUBLISHER

This is the third in a series of books written over the past five years by John Diebold, a pioneer and highly successful entrepreneur in the application of advanced technology. Here, he describes the impact of technological change on the entrepreneurial and managerial decisions of business. The most important impact, he contends, resides in the social changes brought about by technology. These changes are also the least understood. But how business operates and what it does are changing as well—and an understanding of these changes is required to meet the social ones.

The concepts and case studies developed here have been developed by Mr. Diebold over the past decade and a half, and he has presented them in numerous speeches and articles, twelve of which provided the basic material for this book. This material has been revised, updated, and edited—chiefly by Herbert J. Blitz, executive secretary of the Diebold Institute for Public Policy Studies. But attribution to, and the dates of, the original presentations may be of interest to the reader:

Chapter 1, "The Business Meaning of Technological Change," is based in part on a keynote address before the

International Conference of the Financial Executives Institute in New York City, October 25, 1968, and in part on remarks before a Plenary Session of the Diebold Research Program, London, England, September 26, 1967.

Chapter 2, "Where We Are and Where We Are Going," is based on an article originally published in the September, 1968, issue of the British journal, *Management Today.*

Chapter 3, "Why We Are Making Bad Decisions in the Use of Computers: Lack of Appropriate Criteria for Judging Cost Effectiveness," is based on an article originally published in the January–February, 1969, issue of the *Harvard Business Review.*

Chapter 4, "The Next Vital Step for Business: Developing a Systems Methodology," is based on a keynote address before the International Meeting of the Data Processing Management Association in San Francisco, California, November 20, 1964.

Chapter 5, "How to Defeat Technology by Faulty Organization: ADP, the Still-sleeping Giant," is based on an article originally published in the September–October, 1964, issue of the *Harvard Business Review.*

Chapter 6, "Defining Yourself out of a Market: A Case Study of the Machine Tool Industry," is based on an address before the National Machine Tool Builders' Association in Cincinnati, Ohio, May 3, 1963.

Chapter 7, "Taking a Hard Look at How You Define Your Business: A Case Study of the Petroleum Industry," is based on an address before the American Petroleum Institute in Chicago, Illinois, November 11, 1963, as well as on an article originally published in the May 19, 1964, issue of *Printer's Ink.*

Chapter 8, "Good as Well as Bad Use of Technology: A Case Study of the Railroad Industry," is based on the opening address before the Plenary Session of the International Railway Symposium on Cybernetics, in Paris, France, November 4, 1963.

Chapter 9, "When Money Grows in Computers: A Case

Study of the Banking Industry," is based on an article originally published in the November–December, 1967, issue of the *Columbia Journal of World Business.*

Chapter 10, "A Basic Look at One's Job: A Case Study of the Newspaper Publishing Industry," is based on an address before the annual meeting of the American Society of Newspaper Editors in Washington, D.C., April 19, 1963.

Chapter 11, "Computers, Program Management, and Foreign Affairs: A Case Study of Foreign Affairs," is based on an article originally published in the January, 1968, issue of *Foreign Affairs.*

Chapter 12, "New Vistas in Public Service: A Case Study in Urban Government," is based on an article originally published in the May, 1967, issue of *Governing Urban Society: The Annals of the American Academy of Political and Social Science.*

As can be seen, most of the chapters are based on recent writings. But even those that derive from material first presented in the early 1960's contain ideas and concepts so valid today that only certain statistical information has had to be updated. Also, a number of references to the latest events in the various fields covered have been inserted. It is a tribute to the author that these new data and references bear out his original fundamental insights. Indeed, it is a characteristic of Mr. Diebold's past work that these insights are as valid for tomorrow as they were for yesterday.

PART I

Business Responds to Technological Change: The Computer as a Case Study

Chapter 1

THE BUSINESS MEANING OF TECHNOLOGICAL CHANGE

Three levels of meaning that technological change holds for business are evident throughout this book. First, and most obviously, technology changes how *business operates. Second, and often less obviously, it changes* what *business does, even as it alters processes and methods. Third, most important and least understood, it changes the* society *that business serves—and thus creates new business opportunities and alters or ends long-established patterns. This three-level impact of technological change on business decisions presents modern management with enormous opportunity, even as it alters and greatly complicates the process of managing. A central theme of this book is introduced in this initial chapter—that decisions relating to technological change often involve fundamental questions of business policy—even when they arise in the context of a routine choice of one technological route versus another. Failure to appreciate the policy aspects of these decisions, illustrated in several of the case examples in later chapters, can result in marginal rather than full benefits from new technologies and sometimes leads to major business failure.*

This chapter is based in part on a keynote address before the International Conference of the Financial Executives Institute in New York City, October 25, 1968, and in part on remarks before a Plenary Session of the Diebold Research Program, London, England, September 26, 1967.

Business decisions are today affected far more profoundly by technological change than is immediately apparent in the surface content of the issues with which those decisions deal. An increasingly large percentage of all business decisions is today directly or indirectly, yet decisively, influenced by technological change. This situation poses many new problems for business management and emphasizes anew many old ones.

First, even where the problem to be decided is explicitly related to technological innovation—opting for one aircraft versus another or one production method versus another or introducing a product dependent for its success on a new technology—success or failure is increasingly determined by technical factors. These are often so abstruse and removed from the past experience of the executive as to introduce quite new factors into the traditional executive process of allocating enterprise resources among alternative projects.

Second, when the technological innovation is fundamental enough to change not only *how* a task such as a production step is accomplished (the traditional use of technology to increase productivity) but to change as well *what* it is that the business does, business policy questions involving marketing and distribution channels, pricing concepts, and other fundamentals become involved. One very interesting example is the use of a computer and communications system to allow a life insurance agent to "form-fit" the policy to the customer, as well as to keep track of the transaction in the accounts. All too often, as is apparent in many of the cases in this book, the decision relating to a technological innovation is taken on one level, without recognizing the policy implications, and results in lost competitive position or actual dissipation of corporate assets.

There is yet a third way in which technological change affects business decisions. Ironically, it is the most important and the least understood. It is that the social change brought about as a result of technological innovation opens to business its greatest opportunities and poses the gravest of threats. Machines have always been important to us as agents of social change. The greatest success stories and the worst tragedies in business history relate to the ability of businessmen to perceive this level of meaning of the technological change going on about them and the opportunities they present. This is more true today than ever before, and it is this impact of technological change on business decisions and policy that requires the greatest imagination and presents the greatest rewards.

CHANGES IN WHAT BUSINESS IS ABOUT

Before exploring the case examples through which this book develops its themes, let us look at a few of the changes now going on about us—changes that typify our times and the accurate perception of which increasingly determines business success. I have identified six that seem to me of particular importance as well as illustrative of my basic theme.

Business Concepts

The definition of individual businesses will be one concept to undergo change. Peter Drucker in his book "*The Practice of Management*" states: "There is only one valid definition of business purpose: to create a customer. . . .

Any business enterprise has two—and only these two—basic functions: marketing and innovation."

Examples are all about us. The packaging of equity investment with standard life insurance has already begun, in recognition of growing customer need for protection against inflation. A manufacturer of calculating machines should view itself as being in the information-handling business and remain in the forefront of what a few years ago would have seemed unrelated technology, or it may not remain in business for long.

The concept of return on investment with change. Return must be higher in the new fields of business activity in order to justify the increased risk. Failure to recognize this need has led to many bad decisions regarding which applications of the new technologies are viable and worth pursuing and which, in the hard light of reality, will turn out to be marginal. Conversely, business must take bigger risks for sufficient return when technological change is great.

Management may have to take a longer-run view of profits. Instead of planning for a fixed per cent return per year, it may well be necessary to re-orient aims to a percentage of profit over a given product and business cycle. (It is also possible, of course, that, as labor becomes a more fixed cost, there may be a resultant lessening of cyclical business patterns.)

The concepts of overhead and of labor productivity will change as the direct laborer disappears. Allocation of overhead costs must reflect the tremendous and disproportionate increase in productivity of some sectors.

Social Changes as an Active Agent in Business Planning

Social change will result in more profound consequences for business than the technological change that spawned it. Management has always known that changes in social structure change consumer demand. But as the rate of such social change increases—and it will change as fast as the technology—management must be able to anticipate such shifts and react with increasing speed.

The tremendous increase in the standard of living (brought about by technological change) is creating whole new industries in discretionary goods—entertainment, sports, books, travel, service. It is predicted that, by 1973, over half of disposable income in the United States will be discretionary.

The redistribution of wealth, with tremendous growth of the middle class, is creating a demand for higher-quality durable goods. Also, changes in taste will foster redesigning of products. Above all, entirely new products and services will be demanded by a population better educated and more discriminating in its demands. Some of these do not exist today or cannot even be imagined. Others we can predict—for example, individual demands for information from centralized data banks through the telephone or in immediate print-out form, educational services in the home, and financial services as discussed in the case study of the banking industry later in the book.

Shifts in population mix, with disproportionate increase in the old and young, will require new consumer orientation. The growth of suburbia, made possible by the automobile, has created the shopping center. It has brought about not the supermarket but new distribution methods to service the supermarket and the decline in older marketing methods.

Increased leisure has not only created new industries, such as do-it-yourself, but has also changed old ones. In 1968, Americans purchased twice as many books as they had ten years earlier. We now spend more on classical recordings than on our national sport, baseball.

If we adopt the long view of history, we must look to the social change brought about by technology for the real meaning of our current technological revolution. After all, it is to this change that we really apply the word "revolution"—not to the machines. The forces of change are redefining business and management. Insight into the nature of the enterprise and its environment can bring success to the American businessman of tomorrow.

Managerial Processes

Some American businessmen already use computers in an imaginative way, but not many. Most today use them for routine data processing. On any large scale, senior management is only now beginning to address itself to the question of what to do with this powerful technology and to realize that the application of this technology is too important to leave to the technicians.

Dramatic changes can be brought about if people who know the objectives of a business take the responsibility for putting the new capabilities to work. The problems management will face in doing this are formidable. They include developing a new methodology for analyzing the information requirements of a business, including understanding and determining the best ways to design management information systems and how much time and money should be allocated for research in this area, and creating new criteria for judging the cost effectiveness of information and communications systems.

The technology of information-handling, communications, control, and related developments in information theory, at first applied crudely to the mechanization of work already performed manually, contains within it the basis for not only substantially changing the process of management but for extending the range of man's capability. It is a development we are only beginning to understand.

The challenge to management posed by this technology is a challenge of basic theory as well as of operation. It is especially because of moderate theoretical concepts that U.S. business is having the greatest difficulties in effectively putting the new technology to work.

The Development of New Business

The impetus for installing most computers has been cost reduction and, to a currently small but eventually dominant extent, the improvement of management methods. Even while this process continues, the beginnings can be seen of entirely new businesses that depend for their existence upon the use of computer and communication technologies to produce new products and to perform new services.

For example, remote access terminals linked to nationwide (and, already in a few cases, international) computer and communications networks have introduced the capability of selling services—proprietary data and software that allow the unique manipulation of the data to provide answers to a subscribers' queries.

New businesses based upon this concept, which is in a sense a new form of publishing, accounted for about $50 million worth of business in the United States in 1968. And projections indicate that, by 1975, over $5 billion per annum of such services will be provided in the United States alone, primarily to professional users—businessmen, scientists, engineers, and medical and other researchers. Starting in the mid-1970's the development of a consumer market for these services is anticipated. Some of these series—informational, educational, financial—are mentioned in the section on social changes, above. Others may involve entirely new concepts in the production and distribution of newspapers and in the development of individual political judgments and are dealt with in the newspaper and urban case studies later in the book. Thus, an entirely new industry is being brought into existence by the use of computer technology.

The application of this same technology to the educational process will, similarly, create a major new industry for industrial as well as consumer services, thus continuing this particular technology's remarkable process of spawning entirely new major industries that began with the building of computers themselves, itself already a $7.6-billion industry.

Business Planning

Business planning is a combination of entrepreneurial and managerial activities allowing an enterprise to adjust to the dramatic increase in the rate of change. It starts with the definition of the business in fundamental terms and goes on to delineate the specific means by which these ends will be achieved.

Some businesses are learning now that new-product diversification and acquisition programs are often a symptom of management groping with fundamental, environmental change, the real nature of which may not yet have been identified. Once this identification has been made, such programs will be accepted as good business practice, probably within a decade. We sometimes forget how great a time lag there is between companies applying advanced concepts of business management and the bulk of U.S. businesses. While the time lag will continue to decrease, there are those who are only now discovering principles that were successfully applied by such early industry leaders as DuPont and General Motors in the 1920's and 1930's. The fundamental problem is that of coping with a far more rapid and basic change than we have ever known. It presents business with an almost totally new situation, requiring quite new entrepreneurial, as well as managerial, concepts.

A new-product program may be a manifestation of a healthy business that is intent on staying competitively and continuously responsive to new needs and changing desires of its customers. On the other hand, it can also be the sign of a business in serious trouble trying to make up for its lack of a sense of mission or lack of a genuine definition of direction.

Too many cases fall into the second category. Some of the most unbelievably inappropriate moves have been made by otherwise successful business managements. At the end of World War II, certain of the major airframe manufacturers even went into the bathtub and casket businesses, rationalizing that they were using war-found skill to handle sheet metal. New-product programs are an essential element in the healthy and continuing business, but they should be understood as a means to an end; the role of top management is to determine those ends.

Product life is being shortened. The traditional cycle of product innovation is being telescoped, not by planned obsolescence or styling changes but by genuine technological innovation. In many fields there is no longer time to sit back and profit by a competitor's mistakes. We may very well see a situation arise in which it is only the leader who has a chance to make a profit, not those who then copy him, for another basic change in technology will by then be taking place. As a secondary position becomes untenable, the risks of the leader increase; so must the possibility of profit, or he should not enter the field.

The reaction time of management must shorten. The time for leeway in adapting to new technologies has disappeared. Companies must keep track of a number of fundamental areas of scientific work and must react rapidly to apply this work when the time is right. They must consciously plan to be the ones who obsolesce not only their own products but their very industries.

The life of business and industrial processes, as well as products, is also being both shortened and changed. Much of the new technology, particularly that part of it dealing with information processing, profoundly changes the manner in which business is conducted. The increased complexity and tightened interrelationship of functions within a single organization, together with the ever more complex relationships with other organizations, means that successful (successful is increasingly coming to mean rapid) adjustment to change is impossible without a high order of skill in planning.

Business planning begins with an effort to take a fresh look at the enterprise's real role: insight into the nature of end-users' needs and the characteristics of the market and competition and examination of the true strategic objectives of the enterprise. Once this much is established —it must always be re-examined and re-stated—then the whole range of techniques, concepts, and approaches is available to the business planner who actually plans the enterprise, its organizational structure, its financial, production, and marketing structures, and the innumerable ingredients that go into making up the business. Organizational, market, and production planning will thus be undertaken within the framework of over-all business planning. Within this structure new-product efforts make sense.

Private Business Performance of Public-Sector Tasks

One of the most interesting changes taking place on the business scene is the beginning of private business activities in the performance of services, some of which are traditionally the province of governmental agencies. The impetus for this development is the desire to apply to our critical urban and other domestic problems the techniques of systems analysis, program planning, and budgeting and other managerial approaches that have so well served the military in applying new technologies to solve the problems of the service aspect of the public sector.

Much innovation is possible in this process, and considerable thrashing about is accompanying the current experimentation. Numerous contracts have already been let to aerospace and other "systems" companies in such fields as crime and traffic control, urban renewal, education, and pollution. Proposals are already being put forward to turn the fire department function over to insurance companies and the operation of junior colleges to other businesses, such as those that operate the training centers of the federal Job Corps. More than one U.S. industrial firm has already established divisions whose "products" are the delivery of complete new cities.

Innovation in the concept of what constitutes a business, as well as the more obvious innovation in products, services, and marketing, may well be, in retrospect, the outstanding characteristic of the 1970's.

Other Changes

Two other changes are mentioned only briefly because they are dealt with in some detail in one of my other books, *Man and the Computer.* Yet they are integral to the meaning of technological change, to business, and they appear as important elements underlying the considerations in this book.

First, the process of developing managers will change materially. The manager will no longer be able to rise to the top with first-hand experience in every aspect of the enterprise. Change will be too rapid. But the manager will have to be better grounded in the fundamentals of science in order to make decisions on scientific and technical matters. Still, management is itself a profession necessitating special training. The key is in the manager's ability to respond to the demands of constant change. This requires substantive knowledge of the enterprise, as in the past, but the substance is changing very rapidly. Managers will have to decide what decisions should be made—the routine will be on tape. Above all, managers will have to be able to deal with people and their motivations in a changing enterprise.

This leads directly to the second change: *the management of creative and service personnel.* While, in the past, personnel management was principally geared to unskilled or semiskilled workers, new concepts are needed now to deal individually with, and encourage exceptional performance in, creative personnel. There are numerous problems involved here. One is that, when the product is an idea, it is difficult to schedule or to measure and evaluate in all of its ramifications. Also, scientists tend to be loyal primarily to their professions rather than to their employers. A third problem resides in the integration of individualized efforts into enterprise goals. Finally, there are the barriers to communications among different disciplines and between them and management. Thus we are faced with the need for new managerial attitudes and skills to capitalize on the enterprise's investment in intellectual capabilities.

MARKET CHANGES

Correct and Incorrect Definitions of the Market

It is all too easy for an individual enterprise or an entire industry to define its mission—that is, its product or service—in a way that forecloses increasing segments of its potential markets. The markets change when business or individual customers achieve new capabilities and sense new needs, as they use or are affected by the new technologies. Markets defined in terms of old customer capabilities and needs shrink relative to the economy. Eventually they disappear. Chapter 6 discusses the experience of the machine tool industry, which has defined its market in terms of providing a specific kind of hardware rather than providing its customers with the new capabilities they need, as an instructive case study of how to define oneself out of a market. Perhaps the saddest commentary on what has happened was attributed to the president of a machine tool firm in the May 24, 1969, issue of *Business Week:* "Our backs are to the wall. Our opponents, unfortunately, are our customers." Indeed, the industry's customers are supplying their own needs! It should be noted at once, however, that even in this old industry things are beginning to change. Still, the lesson of the past ten years is too good to pass up in this discussion.

There are industries and businesses that have not made the machine tool industry's mistake. They have always watched carefully both what the new technologies enable them to do and how they affect customer needs. There are a number of examples, especially among the advanced technology-oriented industries. Less obvious, less specialized, and, therefore, more instructive is the case of the petroleum industry, discussed in Chapter 7. Not only has that industry pioneered in the use of information and communications technologies on a worldwide scale, but it has so broadly defined its business and its markets that its products have become all-pervasive. Most people still think of the petroleum industry as the supplier of gasoline and fuel oil. But, if we ever have electrically powered cars and solar-generated heating, there will still be a petroleum industry, supplying everything from energy to synthetic materials. It is the creative use of information and communications technologies to improve its products, and distribute and market them, as well as in the continual search for new markets developing from other technological innovations, that makes the petroleum industry an important case for the consideration of the businessman. The industry has moved quickly to avoid the pitfalls of obsolescence and to meet and create new demands for its products.

Somewhere between the experiences discussed above is the case of the railroad industry, the subject of Chapter 8. Many mistakes have been made and continue to be made. But, more and more, private and government-owned railroads throughout the world are looking at their businesses, their systems as a whole, in a new way. Some of the most advanced and imaginative applications of information technologies to serve internal needs and supply systemwide customer services can now be found. The concept of the railroad as a system is particularly relevant to its use of the information and communications systems made possible by the new technologies, in order to improve services and provide new services related to the role of the railroad in an age of proliferating means of transport, ranging from trucks to jets. Most important, however, is the central role of the railroads in serving the needs of a changing society—actually in changing society itself. This has been the case over the past century and can continue, as effective use is made of the potentials that the new technologies hold for railroad operations and markets.

Definitions of Future Markets

Two case studies move from the present into the imminent future. The forces of change are already beginning fundamentally to affect the banking and newspaper-publishing businesses. As can be seen in Chapter 9, by early in the 1980's, we can expect about two-thirds of all the money and credit transactions in the United States to be accomplished electronically. And Chapter 10 shows that, even before then, the job of the newspaper editor will have changed entirely and newspaper publishing will have broadened out into an information-supplying business, with the new information and communications technologies revolutionizing the very core of that enterprise. There will still be money and credit; there will still be newspapers. But the banker's job will be to provide new services and the editor's job will involve him in the use of technologies that will change the editorial product. The problems facing these two industries are very different; therefore, they are instructive examples of the spectrum of change taking place. Yet, perhaps of even greater significance is that these two industries, with such diverse traditions and products, also have much in common as far as the impact of information and related technologies on their operations is concerned. Whatever they have done in the past, their future will be determined by the utilization and sale of the products and services of these technologies. Money will "grow" in computers; so will the newspaper and its related services.

The importance of these two cases resides in the need to redefine the business and its markets for the future. Here, especially, the need to look ahead to what the new technologies will bring—most of these technologies already exist—becomes clear. Of all the industries discussed, none will change more fundamentally and more quickly than banking and newspaper publishing.

Business and Government

Finally, out of the vast and proliferating areas of governmental activities, two are selected to demonstrate what is being done and could be done in foreign affairs and in urban management—and the effects of this on business decisions. The first is discussed in Chapter 11, the second in Chapter 12. Again, these case studies are diverse and again they have in common the use of information and communications technologies.

What government does with these technologies in these very different areas will affect business directly and profoundly. The effects will manifest themselves in numerous fields. They include new ways of negotiating trade agreements and oceanic resource rights, as well as the growth of new relationships between governments and private enterprises for the purposes of serving educational needs and managing urban information flows. Clearly, the case-study approach in government necessitates great selectivity in choosing examples. This limitation, however, is offset, it is hoped, by the specific and concrete nature of the examples. Also, some entirely different aspects of business-governmental interactions in this era of accelerating change are touched on in the case study of the banking industry.

THREE LEVELS OF MEANING

The meaning of technology to business can best be expressed in terms of the facts and concepts of change. Involved are *how* business operates and *what* it does in a *social environment* profoundly affected by technologically induced change. This meaning has been particularly evident for the past fifteen years, ever since computer technology began to be introduced as an increasingly integral part of running a business. However, it has been inherent to business decision-making at least since the early days of the industrial revolution, two centuries ago. It is also the most obvious and easiest meaning to demonstrate and understand. Therefore, although reference to it is necessary in this book, less space is devoted to it than to the levels of meaning that it supports. Also, it is discussed principally in terms of the dramatic and recent changes brought about by the computer. It is not necessary to go back to the steam engine, the telegraph, the electric light, or even the air conditioner.

Changes in the Way Business Operates

Clearly, the way in which we operate a business has undergone substantial change as the result of computer technology. From a few hundred computers used by business in 1954, we have seen a virtually exponentially rising curve to some 56,000 computers in use by 1969. Accounting and recordkeeping were the first procedures fundamentally affected and still represent the most widespread, single types of business applications of computers at this time. Usually, old ways of doing things were computerized and, eventually, speeded up. Many mistakes were made (some continue to be made) but there is little doubt that the present volume and diversity of business activity and the resulting demand for greater accuracy and speed could not have been met without the introduction of computer technology. This statement of fact leads directly to the next and higher level of meaning. Also, it contains an implicit criticism, for change in *how* we do things also changes *what* we can do, and this is still not adequately understood.

Changes in What Business Does or Could Do

This second meaning, although based directly on the reality of the first, also provides the first with its major potential importance. So far as the computer is concerned, the appropriate use of our ability to do things faster and more accurately gives us the opportunity to do new things. From marketing and product innovations to personnel and customer service policies, from managerial control of day-to-day operations to long-range business planning, and from the fundamental reassessment of the roles of old industries to the creation of entirely new industries, *what* we can do has changed. Much of the discussion in this book involves this potential—how it has been realized, how it has been misunderstood, how we can develop it further.

Again, the lessons from the past are clear. The railroad made possible the sale and, therefore, the production of goods that before had had no substantial market. The telegraph made the newspaper a national public-opinion instrument. Refrigeration helped revolutionize agriculture. But these lessons have not yet been applied adequately to the use of the newest technologies, especially those involving information.

The most significant changes in *what* we can do relate to new products and services to meet the new demands of our emerging postindustrial society. These, in turn, are dependent in part on *what* we do with the new computer technologies *within* business, in terms of enhancing managerial decisions. But, it is the *external* results with which we are most concerned in this book, because these results relate directly to the highest, most important, and least obvious level of meaning discussed here.

Changes in the Social Environment in Which Business Operates

Implicit or explicit to the discussion of every chapter is this enormously important meaning. Unless it is understood, the changes in *how* business operates and even the changes in *what* it can do would become almost academic. For business would then be threatened with being shunted out of the rushing stream of social change into the quiet waters of irrelevance.

Yet, this level of meaning is perhaps the least recognized or acted on of all three. Its significance is lost in the day-to-day decision-making of business. This year's and next year's profit-and-loss statements do not reflect it. Nonetheless, the facts of history show that the growth of great new enterprises has been based on a realization, however dim, of the interaction between technological advance and the social environment. Examples abound. There is the automobile; there are radio and television. Probably little can be gained from speculating on what Henry Ford and David Sarnoff visualized in terms of technology's impact on societal demands. The point is that change is faster now than it was four or five decades ago. Precise judgments are needed. Indeed, in their absence, private enterprise may not die, but surely it will diminish in purpose and relative importance.

It is not without significance that several Communist nations find less and less contradiction with their ideologies when they permit private individuals to run their own little shops or plant their own small plots of land from which they may sell the produce for their own profit. Recently a taxi driver in East Berlin related that he was again a *Kapitalist.* At one time he had owned a fleet of thirty cabs: then he owned none and turned in his day's proceeds at a government agency; now he once more is allowed to own the car he drives, but not a second one and certainly never thirty. When the private entrepreneur is reduced to serving the peripheral needs of society on a small scale, his role loses relevance. In the Communist nations, this is recognized. But we have been slower to get the point because the process here is socio-economic, not imposed by ideology. As a matter of fact, it is taking place under the cover of lip-service to an opposite ideology: the dynamism of private entrepreneurship. Yet the results could be the same. For, if the private sector fails to serve the changing needs of society—or is prevented from doing so—a reallocation of resources is bound to take place. This is not a pleasant prospect, either for our traditions of diversity and free choice or for achieving the most effective utilization of our resources. Above all, it is a matter for careful consideration in very specific terms for the individual manager and entrepreneur. What does the changing social environment mean to his enterprise? This book attempts to demonstrate the practical significance of this question.

There is reason to hope that the level of meaning discussed here is beginning to be understood, at least by a number of individuals and corporations. The areas of social change with which business must become familiar and wherein it can serve over the coming decades are emerging. Some are fairly clear to the interested observer even today; some are not. Most appear to revolve around the demand for and application of information in one form or another. After all, the use of information is and always has been at the core of society. Now, the new techniques have made information not only a central but an all-pervasive, moving force.

But less clear are the implications of even newer technologies still in the laboratory. They will achieve fundamental significance late in the 1970's and in the 1980's. They are biological and biochemical; they are based on the integration of electronics, chemistry, psychology, and biology; they involve the exploration of the human mind, the extension of the human life span, the use of oceans and outer space. Legal and moral problems, domestic and international, are already becoming apparent. And these problems—far from being clear and not adequately considered within old frameworks of educational, legal, and ethical concepts—will involve the actions and goals of gigantic new industries.

The three levels of meaning discussed above form a structure. Business decisions with regard to the highest level of meaning—that is, *social change*—depend on the effectiveness of *how* the new technologies are applied to *what* business does. Our environment of accelerating social change demands answers to questions on business interaction with this environment, questions that are only beginning to be asked.

Four major observations can be made that are developed in the pages that follow. They relate in large measure to the role of that most important of recent technological innovations, the electronic computer.

First, information is central to the functions of business and society. The new technologies for gathering, disseminating, analyzing, and using information are radically changing business operations and goals, as well as business relationships with each other, with the public, and with governments.

Second, new methodologies for applying information systems and for judging their real cost-effectivness are needed. The investments in computer and related technologies are vast and on the increase, and mistakes that lock enterprises into ineffective or rapidly outdated systems may be not only costly but fatal.

Third, changing demands for goods and services result from the impact of information and other technologies on markets. Businesses need to look at their real roles in those markets, and this often requires fundamental redefinitions of what businesses do and of the job of their managers and other personnel.

Fourth, the crucial time for reassessment for most businesses and various governmental entities is now. By the end of the decade of the 1970's, and certainly by 1985, new patterns will have been set. The roles of private and governmental enterprises in the as yet difficult to envisage period of change that follows will have been assigned.

These observations can be defined also as the conclusions and themes of this book. They are at the heart of business decisions and technological change.

Chapter 2

WHERE WE ARE AND WHERE WE ARE GOING

The new technology is producing machine systems capable of handling information for any purpose. It is because of this fundamental nature of the innovation—enabling businesses to provide new products and services for new markets — rather than the dollars involved that the computer is such an important example of technological change affecting business and management decisions.

As computer capacities increase and as related equipment continues to facilitate the interface between man and machine, the central role of modern technologies in business decisions will grow enormously. Although the unit output of these systems is fast decreasing in cost, investments of financial and manpower resources in their installation and operation are increasing greatly. Systems are being designed in modular forms suited to the needs of specific industries; at the same time, they require fundamental changes in management concepts, including those that involve marketing, personnel, organization, and control of operations.

The rewards of these technologies for business have already shifted from improved accounting and recordkeeping to economies in production, inventory control, distribution, and other basic business functions. In the future, the benefits will allow management to shorten its reaction time for meeting and getting ahead of competition and for entering new markets. Thus, changes in how *businesses operate is already providing them with the capability of changing* what *they do. The principal question for managements making major investments in the new technologies is what it is they want to do.*

This chapter is based on an article published in the September, 1968, issue of the British journal Management Today.

Invented in 1945 and introduced for scientific and engineering use in 1951 and in a form designed for business applications in 1954, the computer by 1968 already accounted for the dollar equivalent of 10 per cent of all new plant and equipment expenditure in the United States in 1968. It has already changed the nature of many business operations. It first took over the job of recording, sorting, calculating, classifying, and summarizing information. Now, in partnership with new communications devices, it is becoming a part of direct-line operations.

The electronic computer and, in particular, the information theory and technology that have made it possible, represent one of the most important examples of technological innovation of our times. These technologies allow us to build machine systems for handling information for any purpose we wish. It is this—the fundamental nature of the innovation—rather than the sheer amounts of dollars involved that makes the computer such an important example of technological change, affecting business and management decisions.

In some companies, the computer is already playing a vital role in pricing, product development, customer service, and financial planning, as well as in day-to-day operations. It is controlling processes as well as maintaining records and producing reports.

Within the next few years, computer-users can expect to reap the benefits of more-powerful, lower-cost equipment and more sophisticated and flexible management-science techniques. How wisely and efficiently these powerful tools are used depends upon the guidance of top management; therefore, managers need to know which of the technological developments expected in the early 1970's will be most significant and what effect they will have on the organization and administration of the company.

COMPUTER INVESTMENTS, CAPABILITIES, AND APPLICATIONS

By 1975, the average company will be spending more than twice as much on information-systems equipment as it did in 1965. During the same period, its capacity for information-processing will increase more than seventeenfold. A typical, medium-sized American manufacturing company whose investment in computing equipment in 1965 amounted to $3.7 million is likely to have nearly $8.5 million worth of equipment in 1975.

In fact, computer systems are becoming one of the major items in company investment programs, rising from 4 per cent of total investment in plant and equipment in 1961 to some 10 per cent in 1968, as noted above. By the mid-1970's the percentage is expected to be at least three times that of 1961.

The return on this investment can increase markedly for two reasons. First, improvements in equipment design will greatly enhance system capabilities and reduce manufacturing, and hence purchase, costs. Second, advances in software design and in techniques for problem-solving will make it possible to use the equipment more efficiently and take fuller advantage of its new capabilities. But many of the software problems that hamper business today will not be totally resolved.

System Elements, Configurations, Costs, and Economics

The information system of 1975 will differ in almost every way imaginable from today's system. For example, the computer itself will be only a relatively small part of the whole, while today it still accounts for over half of the total expenditure on equipment. Chapter 4 covers this subject in some detail and in dollar terms. Traditional input-output equipment and digital files will continue to be key elements, but image files and communications devices, which did not exist even for commercial use a few years ago, will represent 30 per cent of the total systems cost. These are the two developments that will profoundly alter the nature of information-processing. Communications terminals have already brought about instant access and timesharing, and image files promise a new capacity for graphic communications.

Until recently, most advances in systems design and most reductions in cost were attributable to improvements in the central processing unit. In the next few years, however, we can expect significant cost reductions in the three other major elements of the information-processing system —computer memories and file storage units, communications devices, and other peripheral units. A fourth element, software, is likely to be the exception.

Memories and Files

Manufacturing refinements and the introduction of new kinds of memories, using thin film and plated wire, will greatly speed up data-access time and produce economies in data storage. Cycle time before 1975 will be less than 25 per cent of the 1964 figure, while the cost per bit of memory devices will drop to a mere two per cent. These advances will open up new applications that have so far been unexplored because of economic obstacles.

The by-now-classic medium of magnetic tape will continue to be an important storage device, but disc files will be much more important. Image files will also be widely used, particularly after the early 1970's when, with new thermoplastic materials now being tested, they will become the equivalent of erasable microfilm. Image files that can easily be altered and manipulated will make it possible to process certain kinds of nondigital information, such as engineering designs, insurance policies, and other legal documents, for which facsimile records are needed, and graphic illustrations. Some videofiles, for automatic drafting and design, are already in use.

Communications Devices

Communications equipment, including data-collection devices and modems (devices that connect computer systems to communications systems) will become significantly cheaper. Before 1975, they will cost less than 20 per cent of their cost in 1964. New terminal devices can also be expected to capture more data with greater accuracy, a critical development in information-processing and essential for real-time systems. Inexpensive devices will feed in up-to-the-minute information from a retail store's sales counter, for example, to a manufacturer's warehouse or a bank-teller's window, reducing the amount of clerical paperwork and keypunching and eliminating the delays in information transmission that sometimes limit management's action.

Peripheral Units

Data-collection equipment, by the mid-1970's, will be specifically designed for each industry's needs, like the airline-reservation systems now in fairly widespread use. General-purpose devices will be put together in modular form, enabling users to add or replace elements and tailor the combination to their individual requirements. These devices will be particularly important in manufacturing industry, where they will form the main media for collecting data from the factory floor, sales office, warehouse, and every key point in the distribution process. But, as can be seen later in this book, they also will have major implications for the banking, newspaper publishing, and education industries, as well as for various levels of government.

There will be improvements in performance and cost reductions among other peripheral equipment, which will exist in far greater variety. The most common and costly method of feeding data into a system today consists of document-editing, card-punching, and verification. However, the new technology of fluidics may soon lead to pneumatic card-transport systems; a successful prototype has already been developed. Improvements in optical scanning devices, extending the range of characters they can recognize, will encourage direct machine-reading of documents, and there will be similar improvements in voice-input and response devices, expanding their vocabularies. We will also see more sophisticated visual-display devices, from low-cost desk-top consoles already on the market to full-length wall screens such as those used in government defense systems. Greater use of electronic light pens will enable the viewer to change an engineering design, the draft of a report, or data on file simply by "writing" the change on the screen.

Many of the new peripheral devices will be expressly designed to facilitate the exchange of information between the computer system and its human users—that is, the man-machine interface. The normal product of an information system today is a management report, but in future systems man-machine conversations will be routine.

Software

Unlike hardware costs, software costs will not decrease substantially. While improvements will undoubtedly be made in software packages and programming aids, problems of implementation will continue to limit the full potential of the equipment. Users will have to devote a great deal of effort to resolving software problems, and the average firm will find 60 per cent of its total systems budget allocated for this purpose by 1975.

Improvements can be expected to result chiefly from advances in equipment to simplify programming. Thus, for example, immediate remote access to a computer is bound to speed up testing and debugging of programs, increasing programming efficiency by an estimated 30 per cent. In addition, problem-oriented languages will enable a manager to use the system directly with a minimum of programming training, even writing his own simple programs if he chooses. (This is already done today in some companies; one financial vice-president wrote what is now a key planning program during his spare hours on a business trip.) And, as managers become more familiar with programming, they will be better able to define their information needs to the professional data-processing staff.

System Applications

One result of the technological developments can be seen, of course, in new computer applications. Many of these will simply extend data-processing to traditional functions where automation was previously too expensive to be justified—where the cost of preparing input data was prohibitive, where processing would have taken too long or high memory costs made it impractical to earmark the necessary storage, where legal or operating needs indicated document files rather than digital files. In addition, new capabilities will make it feasible to develop applications for such functions as production-scheduling and budget-planning, which older computer systems were not sophisticated enough to carry out economically. Indeed, economically justified applications will, in all likelihood, be found in areas that seemingly had nothing to gain from computer technology. Three examples indicate the possibilities.

Direct Marketing and Purchasing

Information systems can be a valuable marketing tool, opening up the possibility of direct communication with a customer. A major chemical company uses its system to calculate optimum fertilizer mixes for farmers who buy its products; a cement company is considering providing its PERT scheduling system as a service to contractors who are not large enough to purchase their own. Other companies have arranged computer-to-computer ordering.

Automatic Design

Large high-speed memories, visual display devices, and communications terminals are combining to make on-line draft of engineering designs practical. Car and areospace companies have been experimenting with automatic drafting techniques, spurred on by the shortage of qualified designers and the knowledge that a successful system can shorten the time needed for a design to go from the drawing board to the production line.

Publishing Production Systems

It is now possible to automate newspaper production, from the input of unedited news and advertising to final production of the printing plates. Editors in the future will use video devices and light pens to revise articles and page layouts and to insert late-breaking news items.

MANAGEMENT DECISIONS ON EQUIPMENT, PERSONNEL, AND ORGANIZATION

More fundamental changes will also be brought about by these technical developments. They will include changes in the selection and deployment of equipment, in the recruiting and training of data-processing units, and, most important, in the relationship between management and data processing.

Equipment

Information-processing equipment will be dispersed throughout the organization and will no longer be confined to computer centers. But, whether or not an information system is centralized, its peripheral nerve ends by which data is transmitted and manipulated will reach throughout the organization. The instantaneous access provided by terminal devices will make the actual location of the central computer and data files far less important.

Users will have a greater range of equipment to choose from. Manufacturers will offer a greater variety, particularly, of peripheral devices, and users will do more shopping to select the equipment that fits or is most easily adaptable to their needs.

Personnel

The responsibilities of data-processing personnel will change. Demand for personnel with experience in teleprocessing and communications wiil continue to grow, as will demand for qualified systems-analysts. The systems-analyst's job will undoubtedly be upgraded, since the information system will be the heart of the company's business. But the functions of systems-analysis and programing will also tend to overlap, partly for the sake of better utilization of equipment and partly because the company will no longer be able to afford setbacks caused by the departure of one or two key staff members. Some computer manufacturers have begun training "sysgrammers" in the fundamentals of both programming and systems analysis.

Organization and Control

An important object of the new systems will be to provide management with the means of obtaining an immediate response to questions through peripheral devices. The manager will use terminals to learn the status of particular orders or projects, the sales force to find out what orders can be accepted and what delivery dates given. Senior management will seek quick answers to planning questions, particularly the kind beginning "What would happen if. . . . ?" This will reduce the need for voluminous management reports. It will also lead to greater contact between line managers at all levels and between these managers and the systems staff, which will call for new organizational patterns. (This latter organizational question is discussed more fully in Chapters 4 and 5.)

The system will automatically provide key personnel with information they should know, whether or not they have requested it. Known as "adaptive dissemination," this service is already a feature of U.S. Government systems. The system has on record a profile of each manager, indicating the kinds of events he should know about and the functions for which he is responsible or in which he has a legitimate interest. As the system receives or processes information that meets these criteria, it automatically notifies the manager. This is a long step beyond exception-reporting.

Data utilities are beginning to offer services to smaller companies similar to the internal services of large companies. Giant communications organizations will provide computing power to companies that cannot afford their own facilities or do not need full-time facilities. Even a business in a remote area will be able to take time on a computer hundreds of miles away.

The new high-powered, low-cost information systems will differ in several important respects from most current systems. They will be communications-oriented, geared to on-line and real-time planning and control. The systems will allow quick response to demands of customers (for delivery and invoicing of goods), rapid generation of information needed for internal action (such as production and purchase orders), and continuing, up-to-the-minute provision of operating-control information. These needs do not always call for real-time systems, but they do require an extensive communications network with remote transmission terminals connected directly to the central computer.

All the operating information needed to carry out automated functions, and all the information needed by management to plan and direct operations will be stored in a common data-base at the heart of each system. Currently, even in the most advanced systems, information is scattered in many places, the basic files are sometimes incompatible, and records are duplicated in several departments; even computer files themselves often duplicate information. The common data-base calls for consolidating all this information in a form that will facilitate prompt information retrieval from large-scale, low-cost memories. The design problems of developing a data base are formidable, but a number of companies are now a good way along the road.

The information systems will allow equally for data processing and operations-research techniques. A production-scheduling system, for example, will receive input in the form of sales orders, inventories, and current schedules. It will then apply the appropriate simulation techniques to determine the plant's optimum inventory level and shop production. When it completes production planning and scheduling, it will issue production and material orders. Many companies find that the real rewards of mathematical methods in information systems come from production-scheduling and inventory control.

TODAY'S IMPLICATIONS FOR TOMORROW

Systems with all these characteristics are actively being developed. It will be several years before they are all finally implemented, but it is important for management to recognize their implications. Clearly, advances in information and communications technologies will present management with many problems as well as opportunities. They will, to begin with, call for a new kind of participation by top management. These technologies have come to represent too vital an activity to be left to technicians; management must become involved by setting the objectives of systems development to make sure that it concentrates on central rather than secondary operations. Management must also administer the programs, as it administers other functions. It must, therefore, become familiar with systems techniques and standards and see that these are soundly applied. (Chapters 4 and 5 approach this need from another direction—the managers of information systems must be brought into top management itself.) Further, management must help devise criteria to measure the return on its systems investment. The most important criterion will be not cost savings but profit contributions, so new types of spending controls will be needed. This is one of the main themes of the next chapter, which deals with cost-effectiveness criteria.

New Ways of Doing New Things

In the future, a company's organizational structure will be largely independent of its sources of information. This will mean not necessarily that a company will become more centralized but rather that the decision points will no longer need to be governed by physical or geographical considerations. Through improved communications, the span of control can be widened, leading to a more efficient organization and considerable savings. A big insurance company with 22 regional offices, 71 district offices, and

850 agencies is planning to serve the same number of agents with 6 regional and 63 district offices and its new information system. A large food-manufacturer has already reduced its fifty-plus regional centers to four and, encouraged by its success, plans to cut these four to one.

Traditional departmental boundaries can be expected to blur as, with intricate management science techniques and common data bases at their disposal, decision-makers are forced to consider problems in their entirety rather than parceling them out in pieces. Departmental structures will thus become more closely integrated.

While technology may threaten some products and services with obsolescence, it will create opportunities for enterprising companies to engage in new business ventures. One example is the new data-utility industry. Several large companies are offering data services to other companies and to universities, not merely to gain a foothold in a new market but as an exercise in public relations. A Japanese newspaper company, recognizing that the publishing industry is destined to undergo fundamental changes, has begun transmitting its newspaper directly into the home by television. Similarly, dramatic changes are bound to come about in retailing, banking, warehousing, office-equipment manufacturing, education, and many other activities. To take advantage of the opportunities these changes offer, management must fully understand the direction in which information and communications technologies are leading.

Men and Decisions

The day-to-day management of human beings will be least affected by changes in the decision-making process.

Personnel decisions can be helped by quicker access to records, but by and large the motivation and management of people will continue to be, as now, a human function. However, the management of professional or "creative" personnel will present problems not yet adequately understood. How to keep from leaving their jobs men who are more loyal to their profession than to their companies and more mobile because of what they can do is a matter of concern. In the meantime, most affected will be routine operating decisions—many of which will be performed automatically—now made by middle management, foremen, supervisors, and department heads.

Senior management's decision-making will be affected in several ways. Periodic decisions such as the determination of sales territories and the evaluation of product performance or promotional campaigns will be made more frequently because the relevant information will be readily available. A rather extreme example is that of a pharmaceutical company that now reviews its marketing region set-up every month instead of every five years with the aid of its new system. Simulation techniques will also make it possible to evaluate many alternatives in a short period of time. At present, a company's response to a competitor's price change or to a market fluctuation is usually governed less by choice than by time. Similarly, long-range planning decisions will benefit from logical consideration of many more possible alternatives, and a number of managers will actually be able to conduct a dialogue with the computer to assist in important decisions.

The integration of previously separate activities and a reduction in the number of divisional and departmental units will mean fewer positions for management development. Nevertheless, more general managers or project managers will be needed, at a much earlier stage. On the whole, the manager's job will become more difficult rather than easier, for he will need technical skills as well as experience in line functions, an ability to respond to change when everything moves at a faster pace, plus all the traditional entrepreneurial judgment and drive that make a company dynamic.

In this chapter, we have seen the interaction between technology's effect in changing *how* we do things and *what* we do. Also evident are the *social* implications of these changes making themselves felt in new markets to be served and in the human problems of organization. The significance of changes in operations and how these affect the purposes of business will become clear in the next three chapters. The fact is, however, that, even in this basic chapter on some of the most important technologies with which business must contend, social impacts cannot be ignored. They are inextricably woven into the uses of the technologies and into the business decisions that must be made.

Chapter 3

WHY WE ARE MAKING BAD DECISIONS IN THE USE OF COMPUTERS: LACK OF APPROPRIATE CRITERIA FOR JUDGING COST EFFECTIVENESS

As indicated in the preceding chapters, investments in information and communication technologies are growing enormously for individual businesses as well as nationally; they are equivalent already to over 10 per cent of all new plant and equipment investments. One of the reasons for the still relatively small payoff on these investments in many industries is that changes in technological capabilities and in the level of managerial use of these capabilities have not been related to realistic economic criteria of what is saved and, especially, what is gained from various types of systems applications. Instead of starting with the costs *of processing data, it may be advisable to start with measures of its* value*—the gains derived from the use of the information. Yet the lack of* *adequate means of measuring the* value *of information results, in practice, in most decisions regarding computer use being determined by cost displacement in its processing. As the role of computers changes from bookkeeping to operational management decisions, this failure to develop new criteria regarding decisions as to how computers are used can lead to major mistakes in employing this important new technology.*

The solution to this problem is intimately related to the evaluation of how increasing systems capabilities have changed or could change the role of the new technologies in the business decision-making process. Also, it is related to questions of developing a systems methodology and building an organization able to respond to new information-flows —the subject of the next two chapters. Here, however, the matter of criteria for judging cost effectiveness is isolated for examination. The need is to evaluate not only cost-displacement savings within data processing itself or even operations gains, such as from reduced inventory and faster production, but the until-now "intangible" benefits residing in improved customer service, corporate planning, and forecasting.

This chapter is based on an article originally published in the January–February, 1969, Harvard Business Review.

Now that computers are becoming useful at a higher level of management and for more sophisticated tasks, top executives need different yardsticks in evaluating and planning for them. But this need is not being met. Criteria appropriate to deciding upon the use of new bookkeeping machines—the *cost* of processing data—are increasingly inappropriate to making decisions regarding the use of management information systems. The *value* of the information should be the determinant of system use. Yet, in lieu of adequate measures of the *value* of information, we continue to use *cost displacement* as the criterion. By concentrating on savings in data-processing costs and on added efficiencies in routine operations, management exposes itself to serious errors of omission and commission.

As indicated in the preceding chapter, the business decisions on computer use involve major investments in time, organizational planning, and money for individual companies. This is true also macroeconomically. The latter fact alone makes the aggregate of these decisions of national significance in terms of the competitiveness of industry in domestic and world markets.

THE ECONOMICS OF THE PROBLEM

In 1968, $7.6 billion worth of computers and related equipment was shipped in the United States, representing more than a twelvefold increase over the $600 million worth of computers and equipment shipped in 1960. Indications are that, by the mid-1970's, the figure will have reached $10 billion or more.

About 56,00 computer systems had been installed in the United States by 1969. They represented an aggregate investment of over $20 billion, based on the purchase price of the systems when shipped. On a depreciated basis, this investment would be valued at upward of $12 billion. At the present writing, some 14,000 new computer systems, valued at approximately $4 billion, are reported to be on order in the United States. A large number of these systems is for use overseas. IBM is shipping over 1,000 Model-360 systems a month, a product line that will eventually represent more than $20 billion in value of manufactured equipment over its product life.

In short, computers represent a new, giant industry, and the implications of their use are fundamental to a growing number of other industries, old and new. Yet, ironically, naïve standards are used in justifying and evaluating the machines that so greatly extend our analytical powers.

Until the present time, this shortcoming may have been tolerable. The machines were novel, and applying them at all was such a challenge that management could bother only with elementary cost-benefit analysis. But childhood must end. In view of the massive investment now taking place in the acquisition and application of computer systems to business, more sophisticated approaches are called for.

When we consider the peculiarly sensitive nature of a company's investment in computers—with its potential for a major impact on its competitive position—judgments on how, where, and when the investment should be made assume special importance. In addition, technology itself is changing, so that analytical techniques currently being applied are in many cases no longer appropriate to the task.

Nowhere is this lack of sophistication more apparent than in the way in which computers are applied in American industry today. Most companies carefully weigh the decision, consider the alternatives, compare the relative costs, and then reach a conclusion, on the basis of the wrong criteria entirely.

The problem is not lack of technical knowledge on the part of the experts. Rather, it is the failure on the part of top management to ask the right questions. It is the failure, in particular, to seek quantitative measurements of the very real benefits of automatic data processing (ADP) to a business. This means not cost displacement but rather increased management capacity to control and plan. Such benefits are not being considered in a serious and meaningful way, yet they are today the principal reason for computer use and for moving computers out of accounting and into operational use.

The problem goes deeper still. Because top management has not asked the right questions, researchers have not yet addressed themselves sufficiently to producing useful methodologies for solution. Technicians, too, have overemphasized systems costs and have given relatively little attention to systems benefits to the company as a whole.

CRITERIA FOR EVALUATING TECHNOLOGICAL CAPABILITIES

As we examine the basic problem, we find that the very nature of our information and communications systems, the purposes to which they are applied, the technologies involved, and the relative economics of different facets of ADP are all rapidly changing. They will continue to change in the decades ahead.

The Development of ADP System Uses

The upper parts of the endpapers of this book display stages of development in the role of ADP. The level of management and the level of abstraction at which computers make their greatest impact are constantly rising. Limited no longer to the routine, structured, operational problems of 1955–65, the computer is now tackling the less-structured, more abstract, and more important problems that are the real concern of the highest levels of management.

The lower parts of the endpapers show that evolution in the application of computers requires us to keep broadening the scope of the criteria used in their evaluation. Displacement of clerical costs, an appropriate measure as recently as 1965, has already been superseded as the most relevant criterion. No single criterion has risen to take its place; rather, the need is to include a number of relevant measures. As the computer becomes more and more the servant of top management in the years ahead, the criteria employed in its evaluation will have to be those relevant to its contribution to major policy-making decisions. By 1985, the computer will have become central to the nervous system of the corporation.

The Technological Evolution of the System

As part of this evolution, the computer itself is evolving in a way that is facilitating these more advanced applications, but at the same time it is leading to far more complex and qualitatively different sets of computer-management problems.

We are witnessing extensive proliferation of what is referred to by the catch-all phrase "peripheral equipment" (already a misnomer). In the mid-1950's, this category of hardware accounted for perhaps 20 to 25 per cent of the value of a typical system. When combined with the related communications equipment, it will, by the mid-1970's, represent roughly 75 to 80 per cent of the value of a total system. (The exhibits in Chapter 4 provide a detailed presentation of these changes in dollar terms.) The myriad configuration possibilities of these systems require highly sophisticated cost-evaluation concepts, standards, and controls. Fourth-generation systems will accentuate this problem.

Indications are that the make-up of the information system of 1975 will be almost totally different from the computer system of twenty years earlier, and from the data-processing system of today. These shifts are the bases for new capabilities and impacts of information and communications technologies. The major developments include:

New Equipment and Capabilities

As the findings mentioned above suggest, new machine systems providing increased capabilities will change the nature of management information. These new developments will allow an easier interface between man and machine through improved voice-recognition and response, wider use of improved image-display terminals, and other kinds of progress.

Developments in Communications

Communications terminals and switching systems make it increasingly possible to have the machine system more nearly parallel to the real flow of information within the organization. Direct "conversation" will be carried on between man and machine at nearly all management levels, making currently used printed reports obsolete in many cases.

Executives must be especially careful that they do not purchase, manage, and evaluate the new equipment using standards developed for older, conventional systems. They cannot afford rigidity in this field now, any more than they could when data processing was new.

THE PERFORMANCE OF COMPUTER PERSONNEL

If top management is weak in technological criteria for judging the business value of the machines, it is even more handicapped by the lack of criteria for judging the performance of computer personnel. The unhappy experiences most companies have had in this area have produced high costs; these costs are going to increase at a disproportionate rate. Recent studies indicate several actual or potential problem areas.

First, while the share of hardware costs in the total ADP mix has declined during the past five years, the share of personnel and software costs has substantially increased. These costs often amount to twice the annual hardware cost of the computer system.

Second, the number of positions for programmers and systems-analysts in the United States is expected to double from 317,000 in 1967 to more than 600,000 by the mid-1970's. Since the complexity of newer systems and applications requires that a greater proportion of these more than 600,000 positions be held by senior systems-analysts, personnel costs can be expected to increase even faster.

Third, lack of standards for selection, classification, compensation, training, and measuring the performance of such personnel does not augur well for either quality or cost. Too often, for example, a systems-analyst is a programmer whose résumé is captioned "systems-analyst."

Computer personnel are quickly becoming the major cost of ADP in the United States. This cost needs to be more clearly related to the corporate benefits realized.

THE LOCUS OF RESPONSIBILITY

A particularly significant problem exists with regard to top management itself. From all indications, computer activity in most companies does not receive the serious top-management attention that one would expect in view of the magnitude of the investment and its potential benefits. Nor are the strategic importance and sensitive nature of the investment generally reflected in top-management reporting, control, and operations-planning. This raises the question: Are the right people setting goals for the company's ADP activity?

A recent survey of more than 2,500 executives, undertaken on behalf of 140 U.S. and overseas companies, indicates that technicians, not members of management, are setting goals for computers. This is one of the prime reasons why companies often fail to realize the true potential from their data-processing investment. Communication between top management and senior ADP executives is obviously far from adequate. Exhibit 1 shows graphically the division of responsibilities for decisions among the respondents. Other findings include:

- The average company that responded reports spending just under $1 million per year on ADP activities; 4.3 per cent spend over $5 million and 17 per cent under $100,000 per year.

EXHIBIT 1

DIVISION OF RESPONSIBILITY FOR ADP

(Responses of 2,557 executives)

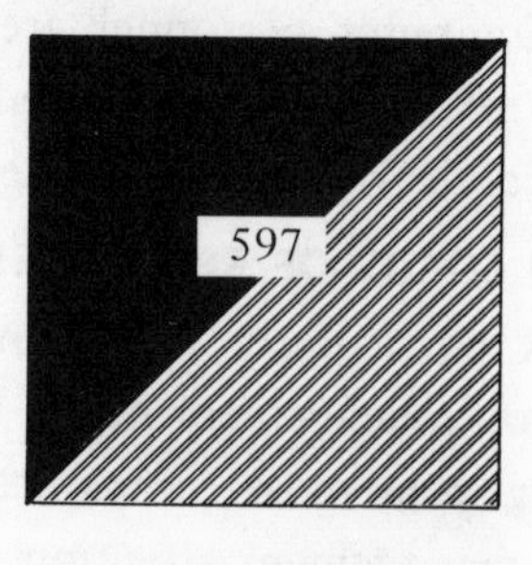

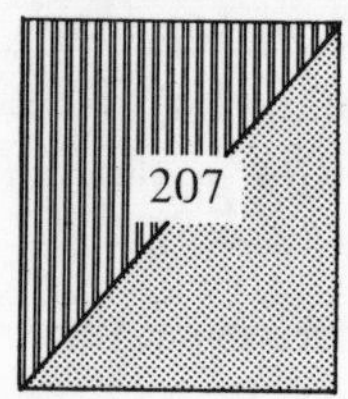

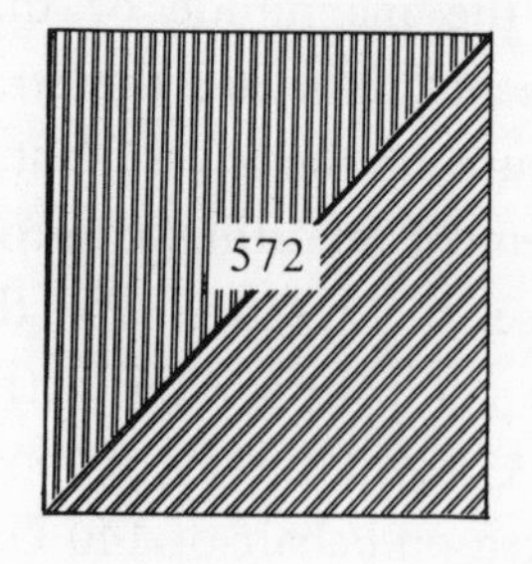

Top management is responsible for directing growth of ADP.

Top management is not responsible for directing growth of ADP.

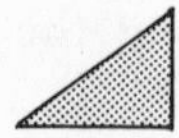
Senior ADP executive is part of corporate planning and strategy group.

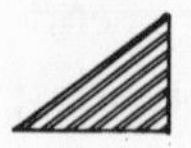
Senior ADP executive is not part of corporate planning and strategy group.

Source: Diebold Research Program

- A majority of respondents say that members of data-processing staffs and middle management have not been successful in bridging the communications gap in implementing new applications. Significantly, 38 per cent state that they consider this "one of the most important problems relating to data processing."
- Fully 79 per cent of respondents report that skill in motivating and communicating, not technical knowledge, is most important to them in fulfilling their responsibilities in data processing. Only 19 per cent rank technical knowledge highest. Communication is ranked most important more often by respondents with high budgets.

DEVELOPING INVESTMENT CRITERIA

As a result of advances in technology, the computer can now play a more central role in corporate planning and operations. But, since present criteria for allocating resources to ADP are based on outdated data-processing operations or on rules of thumb, they do not take into account the ability of computers to contribute to profits or to cut operating costs outside ADP. It would clearly be more appropriate to evaluate computer investment in terms of its contributions to the entire management process.

Undoubtedly, this will be a difficult task. There can be no simple rules of thumb for analyzing a company's ADP expenditures. The latter must be geared not to company size or competitors' spending but to the benefits to be derived in each specific case. Since these benefits often accrue from the value of the information to be supplied by the system as well as from added efficiencies and direct savings in data-processing operations, they are elusive and extremely difficult to measure. Furthermore, modern computer systems are capable of hundreds of thousands of configurations. Highly sophisticated techniques will need to be developed to evaluate all the possible alternatives.

The Analysis of Benefits

The benefits accruing from any management information system, whether computerized or not, may be seen to fall into three categories:

- *Cost displacement.* This involves simply savings in data-processing costs because of reductions in the clerical workforce and other changes.
- *Operational gains.* Here the more complex evaluation of efficiencies in corporate operations, resulting from the application by managers of information received through the system, comes into play. Data on these operations must be integrated into the analysis. Probably the most common applications now relate to reductions in inventory, faster production, and rationalizing warehouse and distribution centers. Also, the analysis of certain reports is showing increasing value, for example on supplier-performance and standard data on customer service—type of service performed, cost and charges, time from order received to completion, personnel involved. Finally, use of market data can be included under the category of operational gains.
- *"Intangible" benefits.* However, most important in the future will be the development of an approach

to evaluating improvements in customer service, corporate planning, and forecasting. Included here is the computer system's role in the company's corporate planning and forecasting and ability to sustain growth and in providing other advantages that may not be present without the system but that depend on management's astuteness in using it.

Many companies today estimate the payback period or make a return-on-investment calculation before authorizing ADP capital expenditures. However, such studies are generally based on cost-displacement savings. It may be acknowledged that operational and intangible benefits will accrue, but serious attempts at measuring the value of these benefits are usually lacking. Such omissions make the estimates grossly inaccurate, for cost displacement is rarely the sole or even the major benefit from new ADP systems. Management may gain important improvements in customer service, in planning and forecasting skills, in its ability to sustain growth, and in other ways (assuming, of course, that it knows how to use the new system).

How can management take into account both the operational and intangible benefits? There is one thread common to both: Each of them is derived from information supplied by the system to various classes of recipients—management, customers, salesmen, production supervisors, and others. Instead of starting with the costs of processing data, why not start with the positive value of the information produced by that processing? The benefits do not stem directly from the fact that given data is processed; they stem from the results of data processing, the value of information in the hands of the user. In other words, the value of information from ADP is not what it costs to obtain but rather *what it can do for management.* Costs have their place, but in a different part of the equation.

Business needs to give more attention to this problem. Success in finding useful ways of handling it would be extremely significant to corporate users of computers and to manufacturers.

A New Level of Analysis

We are now in a stage of transition in which the use of ADP in business is moving toward greater involvement in corporate operations and decision-making of a non-routine, high-level character. Together with the new forms of machines that are coming into use, this transition requires that we adopt new standards for evaluating ADP investment and operations. These points need to be emphasized.

First, present investment criteria utilizing return-on-investment evaluations are not generally satisfactory for evaluating ADP-based management-information systems because they typically include only cost-displacement savings within data processing itself. Thus, they ignore the value of the new information, which, when properly used, opens new business opportunities and allows operating economies. Also, significant savings in both monetary and manpower resources can be realized in marketing, distributing, processing, designing, and drafting. These are often the major reasons for going into modern ADP systems, and they must be considered.

Second, there are no simple rules of thumb for a company's ADP expenditures. These should be geared to the benefits to be derived in each specific case, which accrue from the value of the information to be supplied by the systems, as well as from direct savings in data-processing operations.

Third is the most basic point of all. It is now time to apply management's knowledge of business more fully to the planning and evaluation of computers. In allowing technicians to set goals for ADP activity, management has not been facing up to its responsibilities nor has it been as astute as it might have been in seizing the many business opportunities that could have been opened through entrepreneurial use of ADP.

Most technicians cannot be expected to understand the needs or the opportunities of the corporation well enough to establish goals for computer systems. Management itself must take the trouble to understand what the new technologies make possible and what is necessary in order to apply them effectively and imaginatively. In addition, as is discussed in the two following chapters, the very best and senior ADP personnel must be brought into top management itself. This means changes in management attitudes and, of course, changes in business organization, to provide an appropriate place for ADP within the organizational structure. The resultant dialogues between senior technologists and senior managers would bring both educational and, therefore, operational benefits.

The questions of computer economics raised in this chapter are crucial ones. Top management cannot relegate them to experts unless it wants to relegate part of the responsibility for the future of the business itself. The changes in *how* business does things are clearly integral to *what* business can do. The appropriate evaluation of investments in computer technologies is one essential element of this relationship. Another is the development of a systems methodology. A discussion of this follows.

Chapter 4

THE NEXT VITAL STEP FOR BUSINESS: DEVELOPING A SYSTEMS METHODOLOGY

Related and to some extent basic to the development of cost-effectiveness criteria for information and communications technologies is a methodology of systems analysis. We cannot really know what the technologies can do for us unless we learn how to integrate current and future technological capabilities with business-information needs and business goals in a changing environment.

We need to prepare for tomorrow by synthesizing and expanding current methodologies of systems analysis. Among other things, this means the development of information-flows within the organization to meet new needs; it means avoiding the tendency just to make old information-flows faster and more copious; it means developing an organization responsive to the new capabilities. Primarily it means that management must decide what information it needs in its decision process. The more complex the technologies become, the greater is their ability to serve business needs by simplifying the task of top management in communicating with the computer. On the other hand, this very simplification of routine places even greater burdens of decision-making on management. As is discussed in the rest of this book, the decisions that must be made are fundamental to the role of business in society.

This chapter is based on the keynote address before the International Meeting of the Data Processing Management Association in San Francisco, California, November 20, 1964.

We are today beginning to install complex, new computer-based management-control systems. These systems are different in several respects from the straight-forward business applications of the first decade of computer use—the computerization of punchcard procedures. They involve larger expenditures on more complex machine systems requiring considerably different analytical work.

A salient but as yet little-discussed problem will increasingly characterize and often obstruct, our work with these new systems—the need for a methodology of systems analysis.

The design of management-information systems depends upon major, still unachieved, advances in the methodology of systems analysis. If we are adequately and wisely to use the plethora of technological developments that are descending upon us, we must synthesize a basis for analysis of enterprise-information needs.

Developing this new methodology of systems analysis is the next vital step in turning information and communications technologies into management-information systems. Each new equipment announcement and each scientific finding that extends the capabilities of these technologies further emphasizes the need for such a methodology, in order properly to use our present capability, let alone the remarkable tools of tomorrow.

Stated differently, we are beginning to have the ability to do economically whatever we want to do in the handling of information. Consequently, we are thrust up against that always-embarrassing question: What really are our goals and how do we achieve those that are successfully identified?

When awkward and costly card-handling machines were all that we had available, our time was quite happily filled seeing to it that they performed the most routine tasks. As more powerful systems, more nearly paralleling the real flow of information in an organization, are coming into their own, the paucity of our understanding of what it is management needs in the way of information-processing becomes more apparent. These systems are enormously complicated. A typical example is the multiprocessing computer complex (see Exhibit 2), which is becoming the operating vehicle of the new management-

EXHIBIT 2

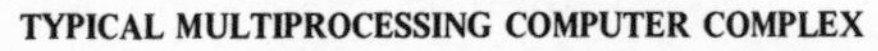

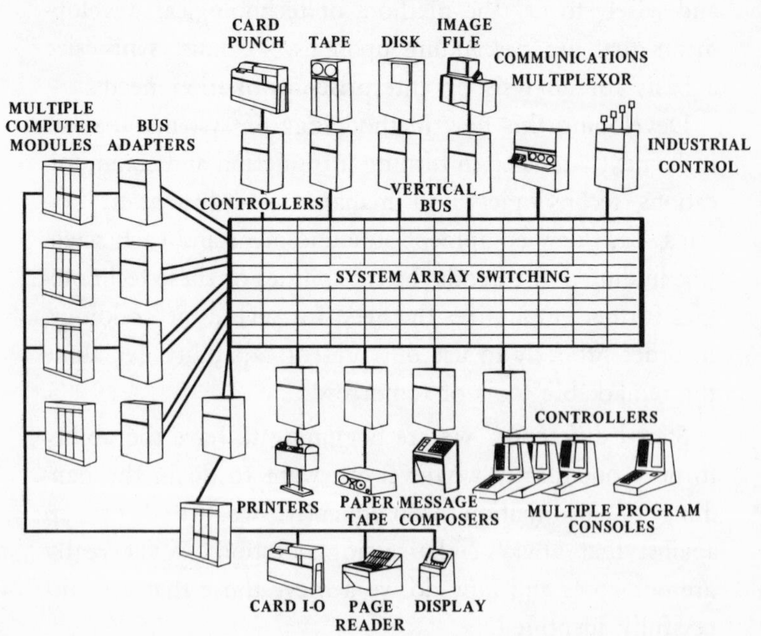

control systems. The longer we wait, as these systems proliferate, the more vivid will become our state of unreadiness—and its cost will be high.

THE CURRENT DILEMMA

To be absolutely realistic, there is today no adequate methodology for systems analysis in general use or on the drawing boards. There is no way to estimate with precision the real current and future information needs of an enterprise in terms necessary to properly use current and future technological capabilities. Nor is there a way to systematically and efficiently translate our goals into action. As a result, systems are not adequately planned in relation to the present and future potential that is at our disposal.

We now have many impressive and useful techniques, ranging from simple forms-design to sophisticated mathematical methods of research and simulation. They include operations research, simple optimization, regression equations, simultaneous equations, queuing formulae, and simulation models. They also include the line-of-balance technique, the forecast-analysis-and-scheduling technique (FAST), and modular and continuous-flow approaches. Yet, separately and in current combinations, these techniques do not constitute a systems methodology that can take full advantage of either the technologies now available or those soon to be available to us.

The Need to Prepare for Tomorrow

The complexity of individual problems of systems design serve to obscure the universality of some basic needs. These can be stated in five major categories:

- We need a synthesis of existing and some as-yet-undeveloped techniques leading to an imaginative new approach to the analysis of information needs and a basis for information-systems design.
- We need to formulate questions and suggestions that will enable management to think imaginatively in terms of what is really required, of just what it is we really want to do, in order to further the ends of the enterprise, rather than using our new-found and impressive capabilities simply to do by a more-advanced computer system what we are doing today.
- We need to combine the results of the synthesis with management's new thinking, in order to formulate a methodology that will organize enterprise resources to reach enterprise goals while, very importantly, modifying and expanding these goals to take advantage of newly realized systems capabilities.
- We need to provide data-processing management and personnel with formal training in this newly realized discipline of systems analysis, so that they will be able to implement the methodology.
- And, finally, as pointed out earlier, we need to be sure that the data-processing manager is aware of the considerations of top-management policy, so that he can achieve a new organizational role as a contributing member of management itself.

The task is really an enormous one. In the effort to create and implement a systems methodology, we must not only draw upon and synthesize the large amount of work that already has been done but we must evaluate the past efforts and the reasons for their partial failures.

If we are to properly use today's conventional systems, let alone the vastly more advanced capabilities for the decentralization of processors, files, and terminals and for voice response image-processing, and lithographic-quality printing that are already on the scene—we must do three things:

- Take an unbiased look at our experience to date. (Let the true wonders and many accomplishments stand, but compare them to where we might have been if we really used the full capability at our disposal.)
- Study everything we know about the nature of systems we now have and will have by the mid-1970's.
- Take an active part in getting the most out of information and communications technologies by conducting individual, corporate automatic data-processing programs as the vital, enterprise-oriented endeavors they must become (rather than passively mechanizing yesterday's work) and becoming involved in industry-wide efforts to evolve a meaningful method of systems analysis and design so that an individual organization benefits today, rather than tomorrow, from the great opportunities that accompany that activity.

Virtually everything we see in the field points up the existence and magnitude of these needs and the enormous economic importance of meeting them.

The impressive rate at which the computer has been introduced into every facet of business and industry has been covered already in the preceding chapters. But there is another factor that points to the need for new approaches. All too frequently there has been a scaling down of plans originally formulated on a sound and comprehensive basis. Would these plans have been successful if fully implemented? There has been a tampering with and an unbalancing of systems design in order to meet extraneous or uninformed objectives. There have been plans formulated too late because implementation would mean the scrapping of costly equipment or the reorganization of procedures that would adversely affect morale and the continuity of operations.

Qualitative Changes in Information Systems

Yet another basic fact emphasizing the great importance of the methodology problem is the qualitative

EXHIBIT 3

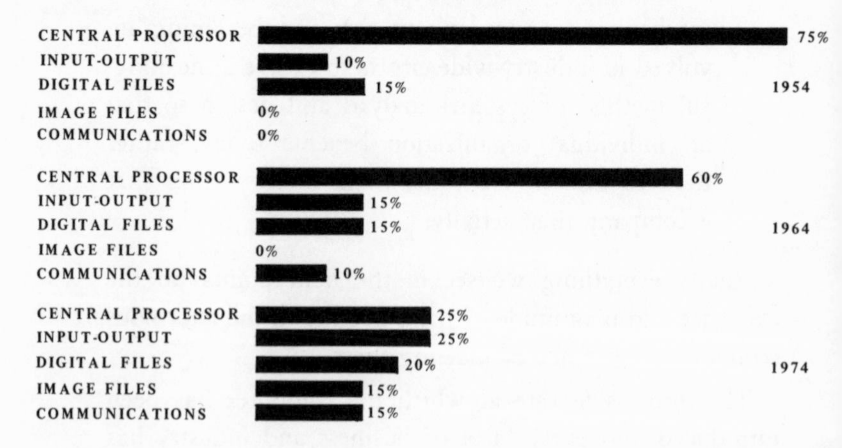

change that is taking place in mechanized information systems as a result of rapid changes in information and communications technologies. Although this phenomenom is alluded to in the two preceding chapters, it is worth repeating here in greater detail. (See Exhibits 3 to 9.)

We used to think of the computer or the central processor as being, by and large, the major part of the dollar value of an information system. In 1954, it accounted for 75 to 80 per cent of the dollar value of the system. Today this is largely changed and by the mid-1970's we will have an absolute reversal of the situation that existed in the mid-1950's. In other words, between 75 and 80 per cent of the dollar value of a typical business computer installation will be in what is called peripheral equipment—in the traditional input-output equipment, in communications, and in such new areas as image files, which

EXHIBIT 4

INFORMATION PROCESSING EQUIPMENT COSTS
CASE STUDY OF A MEDIUM-SIZED MANUFACTURING COMPANY

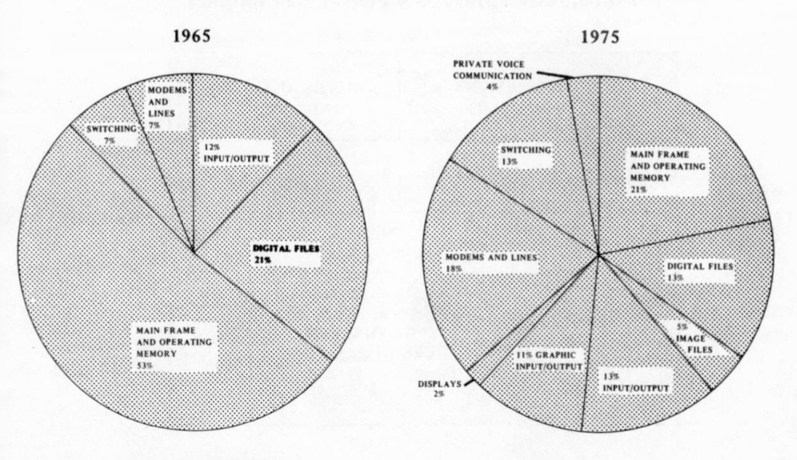

TOTAL $3,700,000 | TOTAL $8,400,000

barely exist today. The computer or central processor will have dwindled to about 25 per cent or less of the system investment.

Obviously this means important change in the industries supplying the equipment, but it also means important change in the character of the systems in which we use this equipment. For example, a significant aspect of qualitative change is the emergence of image processing—the manipulation and handling of graphic images, the display of these images and, more than that, the ability to print them with lithographic quality as output. Thus, these comments are meant to underline the point that is the *character* of the systems that we will be using during the next decade that will have changed dramatically. This means much more than simply that there will be more or cheaper computers and cheaper capacity.

EXHIBIT 5

CHANGING DISTRIBUTION OF SOFTWARE EXPENDITURES

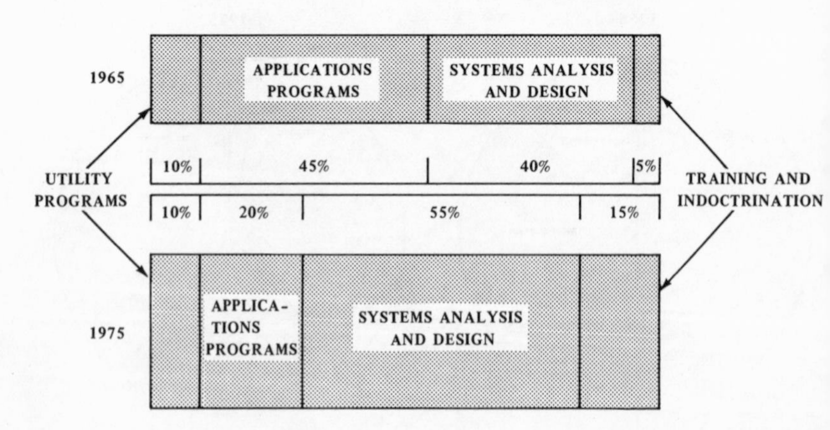

EXHIBIT 6

THE COST OF PERIPHERAL DEVICES
PERCENT OF 1967 COST
100
80
60
40
20
0
1964
'69
'70
'71
'72
'73
'74
'75
IMPACT PRINTERS
OCR
DISPLAYS
CRT PRINTERS

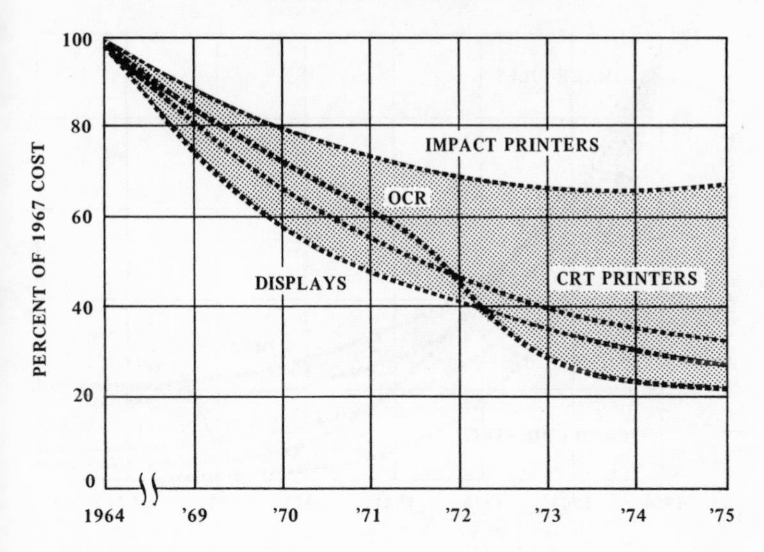

EXHIBIT 7

COMMUNICATIONS COST PROJECTION
PERCENT OF 1956 COST
100
80
60
40
20
0
1964
1969
1970
1971
1972
1973
1974
1975
MODEMS
DATA INPUT DEVICES
COMMUNICATIONS LINE COSTS

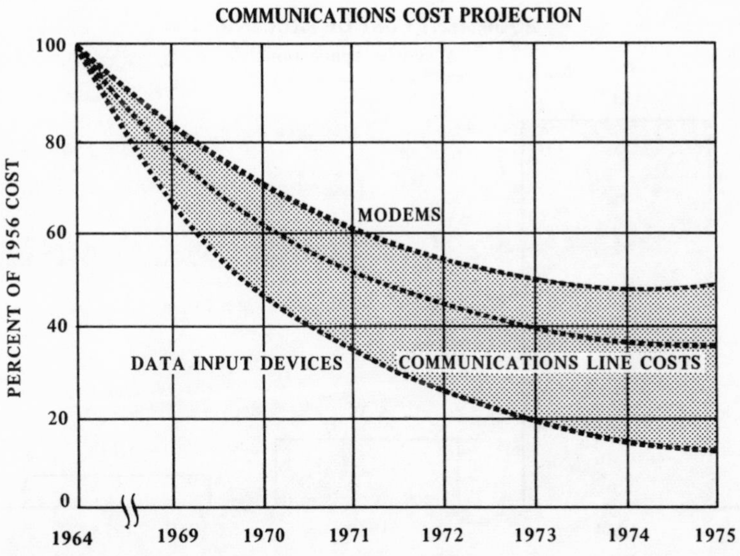

EXHIBIT 8

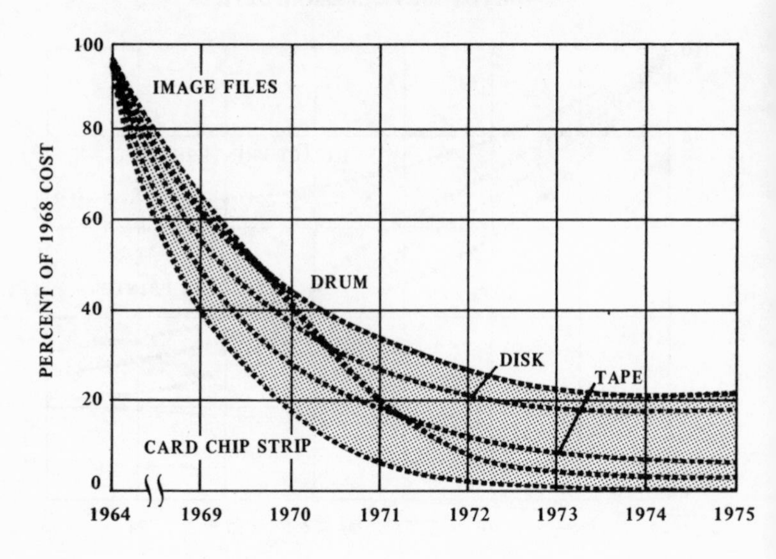

EXHIBIT 9

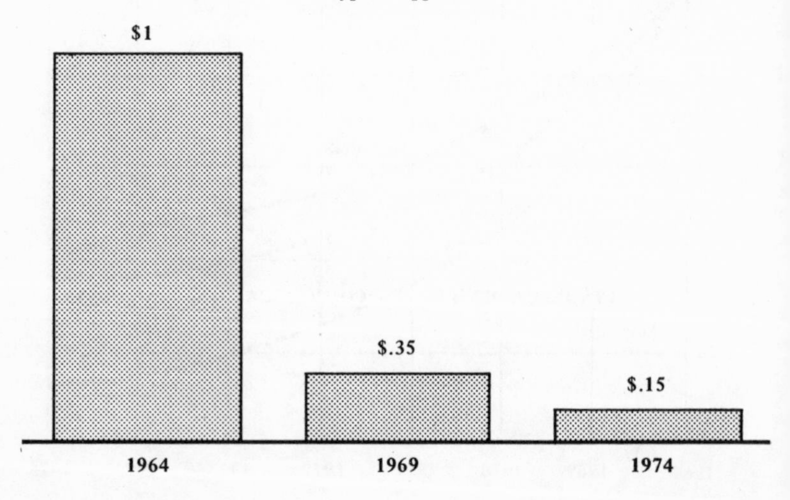

Oscar Wilde once wrote that he to whom the present is the only thing that is present knows nothing of the age in which he lives. This comment is remarkably appropriate to this discussion. It is always a problem for us to talk about how great the change will be in the future from what we have today, but the wholesale change that is taking place and is in the pipeline is striking and demands to be looked at constantly. Everyone working with the practical problems in this field is so conscious of the difficulties and limitations of even today's technologies and the problems of using them that he begins to develop a split personality about the future. One can see major change, but one realizes how difficult it is to use them properly.

There is an inevitability in some of the changes that at first glance seems preposterous—for example, systems responding in spoken voice. Confronted with such changes, one has a feeling of skepticism. Yet it needs to be made clear that these developments are already upon us.

Although the exhibits accompanying this discussion of qualitative changes are expressed in dollar terms, it should be emphasized that it is the qualitative implications of these dollar figures that will really change our business lives. Made possible by entirely new technologies that lead to new man-machine interface relationships, new kinds of files, and simultaneous processing of many different applications, the qualitative changes will greatly increase the kinds of things that it will be possible for us to do with these systems. Provided we can learn how to use these tools, these new capabilities mean major changes in the way we will use information and communications technologies and the role they will play in our businesses.

AN APPROACH TO METHODOLOGY FOR SYSTEMS ANALYSIS

And this brings us to the central theme of this chapter. These changes mean that these new systems will play an entirely different role in our businesses. Work that today seems economically out of reach of automatic processing will, in a very few years, be uneconomic if conducted in any other way.

These changes mean also that ADP will finally come into its own as an intimate, on-line part of everyday management. Our systems are going to follow the natural information-flow within an organization instead of being a stilted approximation of it. Thus, we must at last face the true nature of the problem. We must learn to use properly the conventional systems we have today, to say nothing of tomorrow's technology.

To get from the best of what we have now to what management has a right to expect for the future requires two breakthroughs: what we have called a breakthrough in top management's attitude toward participation in the systems task and a methodological breakthrough in systems development.

To begin in the task we must identify objectives and decide upon means. Some suggested objectives follow:

Involvement of Management from the Start

Since a system involves the entire operation of the company, representatives from all sections of the company should be involved in the system, in particular top management. It is they who should benefit from an efficient information-processing system. And the most effective way of involving top management is for the data-processing manager himself to be part of top management.

Relation of Informal (Real) Organization, as Well as the One on Paper, to the System

It is here that the need for an expanding function of systems analysis in the area of corporate organization is clearly illustrated. Regardless of the success or failure of a functional reorganization, the problems of information and peripheral interest, as well as joint interests, in generated documents remain and must be thoroughly researched and integrated into the relevant systems.

Integration of Vertical and Horizontal Systems

Directly related to the last point is the opportunity that a truly integrated information system provides for cutting across the direct, vertical reporting lines of an organizational structure and involving the more informal and often more effective horizontal information-flow in the total system. Although a vertical system is important for operating control in a delegated enterprise, the horizontal system provides functional managers with vital information for their decisions.

Assurance of Systems Flexibility

Flexibility is required to assimilate future technological developments, changing enterprise information requirements, and differences resulting from turnover in top management. However, flexibility can be assured only through the continuing involvement of the data-processing manager, who must conduct a constant re-evaluation of the system.

Provisions for Crisis Arrangements

The process of systems analysis must incorporate a basic decision with respect to the lines of authority and information-flow in the case of crisis—financial, sales, production, personnel, and so forth. Should crisis arrangements follow regular lines of authority and decision-making, or will special capabilities be brought in or reshuffled?

Maximization of the Effectiveness of Man-Machine Interface

The concepts of exception-reporting and minimum-variable-input-only should be strictly adhered to. Continuous review and restructuring of any ongoing system is necessary to avoid the pitfall of historic motivation for reporting, rather than usage motivation. Simplicity in all things external is often the result of intensive and intricate internal operation. It should be one of the prime goals of an effective system design.

Standardization of Recordkeeping

During the analysis of the current system and the design of the new system, the need for producing standard records of interviews, form-routing, information-flow, and other pertinent factors is paramount. Careful consideration should be given to the tasks to be performed and the relevant information required, before any other investigation phase is undertaken. Forms and question guides should be prepared and used to insure the avoidance of information gaps in the final system design.

Portrayal of Information Systems in New Ways

It is important to find new ways of portraying information systems scientifically. Such new ways should be based on the theory that the world of information revolves around transactions. A transaction is the flow of a commodity from one state to another. Fortunately, commodities are few in number in most large companies and their flow patterns can be charted quite easily. The resulting networks provide a framework in which transactions are related, and they can be used for both identifying and associating all the control centers that are part of an enterprise.

Balance of the Dislocations and Expenses of Initial Changeovers

Minimum dislocation during changeover requires virtual duplication of the existing system and may well involve excessive cost for a nonautomatic system. Should this be the most important managerial factor in a new systems design, then efforts must be continuously made to convert gradually to a more advanced and appropriate system over a period of time in order to avoid the end result being merely an overlaid system. Frequently, the least costly new system, embodying the most effective principles, is the most traumatic introduction and involves the most dislocation at the time. In no event, however, should either cost or dislocation considerations preclude adequate parallel operation of both systems, old and new, to insure performance of the new system. Although the problem of changeover involves a period after systems analysis, it must be considered within the methodology. It is essential that the factors of initial cost and dislocation be balanced with each other and with long-range systems effectiveness.

Development of an in-House Organization Capable of Utilizing and Improving the System

This problem is of special importance as long as there is little formal training inherent in our educational process specifically designed to prepare systems-analysts and to insure a position for the data-processing manager among top management. Every effort must be made by responsible management to assure that the members of the corporate systems group are continuously exposed to all available writings, seminars, courses, and other activities, in order to allow the improvement of staff members, without which systems improvement is impossible. The solution of this problem again is an integral part of systems analysis because successful implementation of the system is premised upon it.

Provision of Adequate Information to Executives and Managerial Personnel

It is vital to the success of any systems design that all affected managerial personnel (and often wage-earners as well) be as well informed as possible on the ends sought, the means used, and the executive directions to the systems-analyst. It is also most helpful, where possible, to have those affected acquainted with *how* the systems-analysts arrive at a new system as well as *why* they do so.

Application of Computers to Simulation of a System

Finally, it is ironic indeed to design a sophisticated electronic data-processing system solely through the use of the imperfect calculator of the human mind and the slow scratching of a pencil, however sharp the latter may be. Inherent in many of the objectives and means that we have covered are the quantitative and qualitative calculations that can be best provided through simulation techniques applying our most advanced instruments. Therefore, at the core of a successful methodology of systems analysis resides the optimum use of ADP itself.

To tackle the problems of a methodology for systems analysis, certain fundamental characteristics of information systems must be considered. Involved are costs, economics, trained manpower availability, time factors, and industry structures and environments. Broadly stated, they involve an awareness that: advances in information technology will greatly increase hardware capabilities and reduce computer costs relative to the system. Speed and range of communications will be revolutionized, and direct management access to the information processed by the computer will be dramatically facilitated; the above technological probabilities are useful to an enterprise, primarily in terms of costs and the economics discussed in Chapter 3; technological and cost probabilities must be acted on with a view to manpower training needs; three to five years are generally needed for an enterprise to fully implement a major advance in its information system; a uniform methodology requires a checklist of systems maladies and possibilities, a statement of objectives, and a testing of hypotheses, all in continuous and close coordination with top management; global (industrial, national, and international) economic factors must be checked constantly in terms of information technology. This involves whether an enterprise, industry, or nation can and does utilize advanced information systems and what effect this has on the competitive positions of these entities.

Finally, it is clear that a prime factor in the successful implementation of systems is the role of the data-processing manager within the organization. The data-processing manager must become deeply involved with the major problems of management throughout the company. He must be knowledgeable about issues concerning sales, engineering, finance, manufacturing, and other areas, as well as accounting. Furthermore, he should be able to think and make decisions on the basis of top management considerations—considerations that involve an understanding of economic and general public-policy issues.

It is essential that the data-processing manager develop a highly responsive network to provide information of a common utility to all areas of management. He must play an effective role in the research and development of the enterprise itself. He must be given complete freedom to explore in depth the problems of management information systems. In short, the data-processing manager must be part of top management itself. The question remaining, therefore, is how to put the data-processing manager where he should be within the enterprise organization. This is discussed more fully in the following chapters.

THE CONDITIONS FOR DEVELOPING A SYSTEMS METHODOLOGY

Current and future developments in information technology combine with increasingly sophisticated management information and systems needs to require a new systems methodology. The objective of such a methodology is to tap the full potential of the technology and to meet new management needs. To develop it, a common effort among users and manufacturers of information-systems equipment is needed. Utilization of what may be developed requires management appreciation of the leading role it must play in future systems development.

To prepare itself adequately for these thoroughly new

information systems, the development of which is inevitable, here is what management could do now:

- Ensure a continuing awareness in its company of the imminent technological developments, some of which are touched on in this chapter. Only by understanding these developments can there be a correct appreciation for the changes in systems concepts that are needed.
- Assure that current data-processing and computer plans are compatible and consistent with what we will (or should) want our information systems to be doing in five years.
- Develop a continuing management-education program that will expose line management at every level, particularly the top, to information-systems concepts and future developments. Direct manager-system interface will characterize the new information systems, and the manager must do his part.
- Support company, industry, and any responsible joint activity toward the development and improvement of an advanced systems methodology. In this regard, there are a number of industry and professional organizations that could play leading roles, each bringing to a joint effort their own specific experiences and needs. One or more working parties could be formed to pursue the following three-part assignment: (1) Compile the numerous approaches to systems analysis, from the simple to sophisticated, as they are tried by various managements, put forward by individuals, taught in schools of business administration, and developed through

efforts of consulting firms. (2) Synthesize these approaches to formulate a methodology broad and flexible enough to serve as the basic framework in the wide variety of situations that must be solved by industry and governmental agencies. (3) Package this methodology in informational or—even better—in educational forms for data-processing personnel and various levels of management.

The need for the data-processing manager to be in a position to make his judgment effective, therefore, has formed one of the principal strands running through this chapter. The informational-educational process required to help the data-processing manager into such a position should be a key element of any action undertaken with respect to a methodology for systems analysis. The finest methodology is only words unless applied. Its successful application is directly proportional to the data-processing manager's power to put it over with top management. And, as can be seen in Chapter 5, that does not mean a sales job. Rather it means being a part of top management itself, one or two steps away from the president or executive vice-president.

While a considerable part of our attention will always be concerned with the management *of* computers, we are now moving into the era that can best be characterized as management *by* computers. In other words, information technology has ended its childhood phase and is beginning to play a vital role in the mainstream of business management. For those who not only have an awareness of this development but plan an active part in making it happen, there must and will be an even more vital role in the fascinating and important world of enterprise management.

The development of a viable methodology of systems analysis is one of the three necessary elements of successful business decision-making that are discussed in this section: It is integral to the development of economic criteria, the subject of the preceding chapter. And one of its most important facets is organizing in a way that permits achievement of its extraordinary potential—the subject of the next chapter.

Chapter 5

HOW TO DEFEAT TECHNOLOGY BY FAULTY ORGANIZATION: ADP, THE STILL-SLEEPING GIANT

This section of the book might well be considered as constituting a series of studies of the business response to technological change, with the computer as the particular technology involved. On the whole, the response has not been adequate to the importance and the opportunities inherent in the technology, and fundamental to this failure is the lack of an effective place for automatic data processing within the organizational structures of most businesses. This problem, of course, is explicit or implicit to the discussion in the two preceding chapters and most of the ones to follow. But here it is examined in some detail. The reason for the failure is very simple. ADP quite properly started out in the comptroller's office where it had its first extensive use. It has generally stayed there, even though its capabilities have far outgrown the purview of the comptroller. And top management has grossly underutilized these capabilities. The need is first to recognize that the problem exists. To do so requires an educational effort, as well as the kind of research suggested in the preceding chapters.

The new technology demands information systems that break through the compartmentalized structure of the traditional business organization, a legacy of the industrial revolution. Many of today's difficulties are the result of the clash of the requirements of information technology with the traditional organization, determining what automatic data processing will do in a senior management function, to be staffed by the ablest men. When top management concerns itself with this function the business has a chance to realize the full potential of this important new technology.

This chapter is based on an article originally published in the September–October, 1964, issue of Harvard Business Review.

As the preceding chapters show, automatic data processing has arrived statistically and conceptually. In this chapter and in those that follow, we will continue to examine why it has sometimes not produced changes of the order of magnitude that was expected. Of course, there are examples of substantial achievement. But the questions still remain: Where lie the roots of failure? Where do they lead in terms of our expectations for the future? Here we look at failure in terms of business organization.

A BRIEF HISTORY

To begin, let us review the record, since ENIAC and Mark I made their appearances nearly a quarter of a century ago. In that relatively short period, seven distinct phases may be discerned in the application of computer technology to business:

- Through the late 1940's, there was little or no thought of business use. Twelve and then sixty computers were considered adequate to handle all the non-scientific applications for computers in this country.
- There was the coldness of potential users in the early 1950's. Typical of this period is the controller who quoted Alexander Pope: "Be not the first by whom the new is tried, nor yet the last to lay the old aside." Everyone had to be shown.
- A brief "status kick" occurred in 1956–57, when corporate presidents decided they had to keep up with the Joneses. Four-color photos of walnut-paneled, deep-carpeted, "showcase" installations

graced corporate annual reports, and yet-to-be-realized savings by computers were what the presidents bragged about to one another on the golf course.

- With the onset of the 1957 recession came disillusion, as the initial installations failed to live up to expectations. Naïve early projections of big payoffs changed in a matter of months to the hope only to break even.
- The fifth era was ushered in during the early 1960's. It was characterized by a growing sophistication on the part of business regarding at least the obvious data-processing applications, as more programmers and other trained personnel became available. Of special importance, there was a growing appreciation by computer manufacturers of business–data-processing problems that affected computer design.
- By the mid-1960's, we had routine acceptance of the electronic computer as an everyday tool of business. Some 20,000 computer systems were installed in this country alone. Third-generation systems were announced with great fanfare. The problems they engendered frustrated many, appalled some, but caused few really to give up. It was a time of testing for today and the future.
- Finally, by the start of 1969, 56,000 computer systems were installed in the United States. A fourth-generation was quietly beginning to develop, as the bugs of the third were being worked out, and as examples of really advanced applications or, at

least, concepts became more widely discussed. Yet, as we have seen already, we are far from realizing the potential of the computer in management.

THE UNREALIZED POTENTIAL

Of course, many of the 56,000 ADP systems in use are more than paying their way, and some are performing tasks that were not possible before. But even in the best applications we have not come close to realizing the computer's true potential. Of course, deterring factors differ from installation to installation. Sometimes—but rarely now—the equipment is at fault. In most cases the problem can be laid right on management's doorstep. Some of the reasons we have already discussed in the preceding chapters may be summarized in the following way:

- Inadequate planning, mostly parochial rather than corporation-wide in scope.
- Not enough creative thinking and too much reliance on canned approaches.
- Selection of the wrong people to plan the installation—that is, technical specialists who fail to acknowledge, or even appreciate, their limited understanding of business practice.
- Overemphasis on hardware and underemphasis on the design of comprehensive systems.
- Very limited and misleading criteria of cost effectiveness.

The Current Place of ADP in the Organization

These are serious faults. But there is a basic problem that seems to underlie them. It is far more subtle, yet in a paradoxical way it could not be simpler: We still have no place for ADP in our organizational structures.

Machine accounting has been with us for many decades, performing a vital role in the operation of our businesses. Machine accountants were the first to become aware of computer potential because computers were originally manufactured and supplied mainly by the builders and sellers of punched-card accounting equipment. Accountants attended the manufacturers' schools. They learned the new vocabulary of scientific terms—"floating decimal," "binary bits," "redundancy checks"—and became "computer experts." Thus, they became a ready-made repository for the ADP function.

Most computer installations were lodged amid a jungle of punched-card peripheral gear. Conversion of existing punched-card applications seemed to be the natural avenue to the world of tomorrow. Payroll handling was the favorite for conversion, despite the already high efficiency of tab methods for it. The case seemed closed; the responsibility for ADP was "logically" assigned to the assistant comptroller in charge of machine accounting.

Plausible as the move may have seemed at the time, it got many companies into trouble. The assistant comptroller may do a commendable job in the areas for which he is normally accountable. But his new ADP role frequently places him in an unfamiliar position where he can do neither himself nor his organization much good. True, some computer systems can be justified on the basis of their clerical savings, which are usually the assistant comptroller's prime preoccupation. However, as we have discussed, it is the vision of improved management control through a highly responsive, organic business-information system that should attract imaginative management to the new potential of computers and that can pay off handsomely in the end.

Information technology now provides the long-needed capability for timely analysis of and instantaneous control over ever more complex operations. With its fantastic speeds, tremendous flexibility and versatility, and capacity for handling multiple, interrelated variables, ADP is today literally the only means of counteracting the monolithic bureaucracy of our giant institutionalized organizations. It is ironic that this new resource is passed up by most of management, not because of the limitations of the technology—for information technology has already far outstripped our apparent ability to apply it—but in large part because of our organizational structures themselves.

Assistant comptrollers equipped with the best computers in the world are not going to make the vision of applied information technology a reality very often. They are buried too deep in one leg of the business. They lack authority. Their departmental position arouses the antipathy of their peers, to say nothing of that of the thrice-removed functional vice-presidents, the even tenor of whose ways ADP must inevitably disturb. But, most important of all, they lack the entrepreneur's view of the enterprise as a whole.

The situation may well continue to deteriorate. Conditions that aggravate the problem today show signs of building up to an intolerable impasse in many organizations before long. The managements of these organizations are still conceptually unprepared for the revolution that will take place in information technology during the early 1970's. Although the computer arrived in the 1950's, its use in most companies is stall characterized by a lack of imagination and inspiration. There, executives are doing little more with ADP than adding speed and economy to tasks performed with earlier equipment. They are simply putting wheels under existing systems and procedures.

The Shape of the Future

To understand the speed and force with which information technology is moving, let us look at just a few of the advanced applications, some of which have already been discussed in greater detail.

1. By the mid-1970's, we shall see the commercial perfection of man-computer communications. Programming languages by then will be more like everyday language, and man will use voice communication and visual communication to direct computers.

2. "Polymodular" or multiprocessing-and-programming systems will be a *common* mode of design. Systems modules (functional "packages" of equipment) will perform in a number of ways: They will work separately or in tandem, communicate with a great variety of input and output devices, and process a great many programs simultaneously.

3. Programs will incorporate self-correcting features, permitting the machine to recognize its own malfunctions, correct them, or select a different path to solve a problem.

4. By the end of the 1970's, heuristic or self-organizing systems will allow machines to develop, on their own, problem-solving methods best suited to the management

analysis of the problem at hand. These systems will help achieve the goal of dispensing with formal programs altogether for certain decision-making processes handled by machine. The machines will tend more and more to "think," in the accepted meaning of that word.

As a consequence of such developments, management will never be the same again. The ADP system will gradually encompass more and more of the business structure. The distinction between the control system of the plant—where over-all, on-line computer control is already a reality in electric utilities, steel-rolling mills, and petroleum refineries—and the ADP system of the office will disappear. One information system will feed the entire business. This system will be the arteries through which will flow the lifestream of the business: market intelligence, control information, strategy decisions, feedback for change.

The new information systems will not be merely more-mechanized versions of most of today's computer applications, which are themselves simply perpetuations on tape of yesterday's punched-card runs. The on-line multiprocessing system, linking many remote sites together through a digital communications net, is a total departure from today's computerized tab rooms.

The most common information-systems hardware requirements of the future will differ markedly from today's installations. We will see the development of factory-office control systems and of sophisticated capturing of far-flung source data, including document-reading, voice recognition, library-information retrieval, translating machines, gaming simulators, and a host of entirely new kinds of machine systems.

The rate and magnitude of the changes already taking place dramatically highlight the indispensability of top-management participation in ADP planning; business imagination, analytical ability, and entrepreneurial flair will have to be exercised to apply these new systems effectively. Managements must not delude themselves by viewing these developments as the natural evolution of new generations of business machines. The developments will comprise a conceptual revolution, not an improvement in hardware.

CREATING A PLACE FOR ADP

Unfortunately, most managements are, in fact, improperly prepared for ADP to an alarming degree. The first and most important step is to recognize that a problem exists, which will in itself take time. It will involve the education of first-class managers in the potential of information systems. Younger managers must be developed in an environment in which information technology does not mean the back office of the accounting department but rather the main route to top-level line or staff responsibility. Within the past two years, the stockbroker's back office has become a major front-office problem.

Collaterally, a genuine business-research effort will be made mandatory. Although the role of engineering and scientific research is fully appreciated today, only trifling sums are allocated for research in the business-management processes themselves.

Once these efforts of management education and research are under way, the task of creating a place for ADP in the organizational structure can be approached. This is no simple task. Today's business organization is really a legacy of the industrial revolution: Specialization of labor has been followed by organization *around* specialties.

However, the new technology makes it imperative that we build information systems that break through the compartmentalized structure of traditional business organization. It is not necessary to belabor the potentials for conflict in such a course. It is no mere coincidence that many of the difficulties experienced thus far in ADP have resulted from the clash of the requirements of information technology with our traditional organizational system.

We can only speculate on the final outlines of the solution. Perhaps a new management function will arise. It may consist of the design, economic evaluation, installation, programming, continual reprogramming (so long as this is necessary), and operation of the total business-information system. It would link the traditional activities of market analysis, product development, sales effort, and accounting control. Whether this would be a staff or line function is a moot and perhaps academic question. But it will surely be a senior-management function staffed by the ablest men the business can find. Only if conceived and organized in this way can it help the organization realize the full potential of ADP.

The organizational questions discussed in this chapter appear to underlie the crucial needs to develop adequate criteria of cost effectiveness and a systems methodology, which are the subjects of the two preceding chapters. The links among these needs should now be clear, because the first two must be met by top management, and only if ADP becomes a true concern of top management can this occur.

The chapters that follow, on redefining a business and on using technological change to create new enterprise opportunities, illustrate through specific case studies the extent to which policy decisions—as well as procedural changes—determine the yield that is obtainable from new technologies. Thus, we move from the fundamentals of economics, methodology, and organization to the essential functions and purposes of business: defining, holding, creating, and serving the market.

PART II

Managing a Business to Benefit Most from Technological Changes: Three Case Studies

PART II

Managing Resources to Benefit Most from Technological Changes: Three Case Studies

Chapter 6

DEFINING YOURSELF OUT OF A MARKET: A CASE STUDY OF THE MACHINE TOOL INDUSTRY

The machine tool industry, on the whole, has in the past narrowly defined itself as "builders of metal-cutting and metal-forming machines," rather than as suppliers of manufacturing systems and capabilities for all industries. This definition draws attention to the failure to appreciate that policy as well as technical and product issues are involved in the business response to technological change and presents us with a good case study illustrative of a basic theme of this book. The result has been a relative decline of the industry's position in the economy, a loss of customers who now either supply their own needs or buy from other countries, and a questionable future if current practices persist. A symptom of the industry's problems is the fact that few if any of the small number of innovations the industry actually does use originated within the industry itself.

The need is for increased research into the new technologies that the industry could develop, business planning, the study of customer needs in depth, and the development of capabilities to attract research-and-development contracts. But most important is the need for entrepreneurial and managerial innovations to redefine the business and reorganize the companies and their marketing programs.

This chapter is based on an address before the National Machine Tool Builders' Association in Cincinnati, Ohio, May 3, 1963.

Technology's impact on *how* business operates and on *what* it does in a changing social environment is illustrated first by the rather negative experiences of the machine tool industry. It is only fair to say that things are *beginning* to happen in this industry. Business planning and the requirements of entrepreneurial, managerial, and technological innovation are being understood by a small but increasing number of companies. Over the past five years there has been some growth—not as much as should have been possible, as we shall see, but some. Also a limited amount of diversification, consolidation, and acquisition has taken place. The industry has grown at least potentially stronger. However, the point of this case study revolves around what has *not* taken place, the unrealized potential, the opportunities passed up by the failure to appreciate that *policy* as well as technical and product issues are involved in the business response to technological change. And this point, unfortunately, is illustrated well by the machine tool industry as a whole.

Specifically, technological change often requires a rethinking of the purposes of a business. This leads to business decisions responding to the market to be served: defining the market, meeting the new demands of the market, in some cases actually creating the market.

Indeed, as is noted in the following pages, it looks as if business is good for the machine tool industry. The past decade of prosperity could have enabled the industry to consolidate its position and establish the basis for expansion in the years to come. It may not, however, represent any more than just another cyclical upswing, because this time has not been used—as previous periods had not been

—to take a searching look at the machine tool business.

The business of supplying machine tools should be in the midst of a revolution. Unfortunately, it is a revolution that has thus far failed to take place. Actually, a sort of revolution affecting the industry and its markets has taken place, but the industry has been its victim rather than its master. This need not have been the case, but it will remain true until there is widespread recognition that a revolution necessitates major innovations: *entrepreneurial innovations, managerial innovations,* and *technological innovations.* This, in brief, is the burden of this chapter.

ENTREPRENEURIAL INNOVATIONS

Of the three kinds of innovation that the industry requires, entrepreneurial innovation will be the hardest to bring about because it involves rethinking and redefining of the industry. To begin, there are the following questions:

- How does the industry define its business?
- What problems are posed by such a definition?
- How should it define its business?

Defining One's Business

When one takes the opportunity to visit the machine tool industry's plants and to talk with the managements, and also when one takes the opportunity to talk with the customers, an observation of special interest is the way in which this industry views itself. For the sake of argument, let us overstate the case.

Although machine tools are defined as power-driven machines used to shape or form, by cutting, impact, pressure, or electrical techniques, the industry most often seems to view itself as "builders of metal-cutting machines or of metal-forming machines." There is strong resistance to widening this definition to manufacturing machines. In spite of the fact that the term "machine tools" has come to embrace a much wider variety of industrial machinery, the industry appears to take special pride in the building of boring machines, milling machines, lathes, punch presses, or some other functionally specialized tool.

The term "builders" conveys much about the way in which the industry thinks of itself. It does not use even the word "suppliers," certainly not "marketers," but "builders": "builders" on order, *filling* customer *orders* with a high-precision product, builders of tools for skilled artisans, designers for the craftsman.

And what is wrong with such a view? It is too limited. A fine product is built with a *problem,* as well as a craftsman, in mind. The current definition paints the industry into a corner—a corner of relatively decreasing size in American business and decreasing relevance to an economy revolutionized by technological change.

The Role of the Industry in the Economy

Let us first look at some data that appear fairly favorable until subjected to some analysis. Between 1940, the last prewar year, and 1968, the gross national product in current dollars increased about ninefold. Machine-tool-industry production increased nearly sevenfold over the same period, representing only a slight decline as a percentage of GNP. But closer inspection reveals three important problems about the machine tool industry:

- A dangerous dependence on cyclical swings of the economy

- A decreasing share in business expenditures on plant and equipment for durable goods
- An increasing reliance on the sale of products—especially numerically controlled machine tools—that originated from innovations *outside* the industry

The following statistics bear out this analysis. Between 1940 and 1961, the beginning of the great capital-spending boom of this decade, machine tool production actually declined from a 0.4 to a 0.15 per cent share of GNP. Since then the share has increased once more to 0.3 per cent. Obviously, however, the industry is subject to sharper swings than the economy as a whole, a fact that is evident from similar data relating to the Korean War years.

Although machine tool production from 1961 to 1968 increased at a rate slightly faster than business expenditures on plant and equipment for durable goods, it has never caught up with what has been lost since 1940, when it was equal to about one-half of such expenditures. In 1961, machine tool production represented 13 per cent of these business expenditures. By 1968, it had climbed back to barely 21 per cent.

Finally, over the past ten years, some 21,000 machines, which had their original development outside the industry, were shipped: electrical-discharge, electric-chemical, ultrasonic cutting, high-energy-rate forming, and numerically controlled (NC). Although this represented only about 2 per cent of all metal-cutting and metal-forming machines shipped, NC machines in 1967 alone represented 27 per cent of the *value* of all machine tools shipped.

Why is this occurring? The third problem listed above (reliance on developments outside the industry) is discussed under the heading of *technological* innovation, but the first two can be put squarely under this heading of *entrepreneurial* innovation.

Metal cutting and forming account for a continuously decreasing portion of our gross national product. First, an increasing portion is accounted for by the working of nonmetallic materials. Metal cutting and forming excludes many important production processes: welding, casting, molding, extruding, and powder metallurgy. The growth of plastics such as nylon, teflon, delrin, and polyethylene as materials is as important as industrial output. It has sent into eclipse the absolute dollar gains in metal cutting and forming by making them a decreasing percentage of total manufacturing equipment gains.

Second, metal-working industries are constantly striving to reduce the amount of metal-cutting they have to do. In this effort, they have the cooperation of a number of other industries, including the materials suppliers. The metal suppliers provide metals extruded to semifinished form. Metal companies also provide precision forgings and precision castings, as do independent foundries and forge shops. The point is that, even in cases where metal has not been replaced, it is often being used in a form that permits a dramatic reduction in the amount of machining needed and a consequent reduction in the need for machine tools.

In other words, metal cutting and forming are techniques that tend to be engineered out of products and processes. And metal is a material that, with the active engineering support of nonmetallic-material suppliers, is frequently replaced in product designs. *Thus, the industry is not getting its share of the capital-goods market.*

The Service of Customer Needs

What does definition of a business have to do with such a decline? How should a business be defined? Thought should be given to defining this business *as suppliers of manufacturing systems and capabilities to all industries.* Customers' needs should dictate the business. The business should be market-oriented and receptive to technological inputs, from many quarters, that help to serve customers' needs. The aim should be to provide customers with a *manufacturing capability*—not only a particular, functionally oriented, metal-working tool but also the ability to make a product.

It is commonplace to say that this is a small industry and that any one of its companies has few competitors. It is a small industry and it stays small precisely because the business is defined in a way that keeps it small. There are only a few competitors, if one looks only to the other companies in the industry as presently defined: builders of turning machines, milling machines, or grinding machines. But there could be a very large industry if it were defined in a large way. A total of $65 billion was spent on new plant and equipment in 1968.

The machine tool industry has lost much of its business because it has refused to supply what the customer wanted. A recent survey shows that a major percentage of its customers engineer and build all or some of their new manufacturing equipment. As late as May, 1969, the president of a machine tool company was quoted as saying,

"Our opponents, unfortunately, are our customers." Where applicable equipment is not available through the builders, in-plant engineering personnel are designing and building it themselves.

There are many competitors, if recognition is given the facts for what they are, for other industries are today fulfilling customers' needs. The competitors are not located in Fond du Lac, Milwaukee, Bridgeport, Springfield, Cincinnati, or Rockford. They are located in Los Angeles, Seattle, San Diego, Detroit, Philadelphia, Pittsburgh, Wilmington, and Boston and on Long Island. The textile industry for years thought its competition was the firm across the street in Lowell or in Fall River. It woke one morning to realize that its customers' needs were being filled by a chemical manufacturer in Wilmington.

Business Planning

The machine tool industry's companies are known and trusted names in American industry. They are the firms to which an expanding America could turn with confidence. Yet the industry defines its field so narrowly that it remains a small industry. There is no need for that. For example, North American Aviation realized years ago that the air-frame industry was, in many ways, faced with problems similar to those of the machine tool industry. At that time, they undertook some of the most imaginative business-planning ever and made carefully planned decisions to build their business in new ways and they built their own capacity in these areas—in electronics, in atomics, in rocket engines. They established divisions in each of these fields at a time when few others could see in them any future at all worthy of a great air-frame manufacturer. Today, their electronics division alone accounts for a volume of business each year nearly as large as the entire machine tool industry. A second electronics division was started recently in a still newer area and is already accounting for sales equal to an appreciable portion of the size of machine tools.

Success of this nature need not be limited to electronics. Individual new companies, for example, Xerox and Polaroid, started in the seventieth, eightieth, or one hundredth year of some of the machine-tool-industry companies' histories, with far less in the way of resources and name. In a few years, they will equal virtually the entire output of the machine tool industry. General Electric, IBM, and any number of other companies have done the same in a variety of fields created by using new technologies to fill customer needs, to serve the new markets created by technological change itself.

The important thing is that they defined their business in a different way. T. J. Watson, president of IBM, defined his business by saying, "Service is our business." General Electric says, "Progress is our most important product." These are not idle advertising phrases; they have content and meaning for the men who built these organizations.

Thus, entrepreneurial innovation seems to be the prime need of the machine tool industry. This means the need to develop new products with greater capabilities; it means the need of a broader range of equipment able to solve a variety of manufacturing problems; it means the need to deliver to the customer a manufacturing capability. This industry could spark revolutions in American manufacturing. Thus, it could regain its share of the enormous growth that is yet to come in American industry.

We are entering an era of the greatest conceivable change in the manufacturing methods of American industry. An industry such as machine tools could play a vital and important role in this expansion period. But its business must be defined in the right way, as suppliers of manufacturing systems and capabilities to *all* industry. This definition will then require the support of aggressive marketing and product development.

MANAGERIAL INNOVATIONS

The second kind of innovation is managerial innovation. Numerous managerial innovations are necessary if the industry is to thrive and to prosper. For example:

- Establishment of an organizational structure that not only allows but encourages technological innovation and that insures technological inputs from many sources outside the industry.
- Creation of an atmosphere that looks outward, not inward—a washing of the corporate and industrial windows to provide a better view of what the customers want.

These and other important and interesting innovations are characteristics of the major managerial change that must and will take place in this industry. But the key managerial innovation (if we treat business planning as an *entrepreneurial* innovation) resides in marketing. Specifically, creative marketing in the machine tool industry encompasses the following.

Study of Customer Needs in the Widest Possible Sense

Marketing innovations do not mean harder selling, they mean *smarter* selling. In other words, creative marketing comes from an understanding of customer needs. The material suppliers—such as the metal companies—only recently discovered the advantages of understanding user problems and the effect this can have on their business. Companies like IBM have understood this for many years and have built their business in this manner.

Once the machine-tool-industry business is defined as serving to supply manufacturing capabilities, there is much to gain by constantly anticipating user needs. The wild fluctuations of the industry's business cycle, though understandable in terms of the heavy equipment cycle, are not to be viewed only as conditions that exist, God-given, but as a problem to be solved. For, when the fate of the entire industry is tied to these fluctuations, this is not a sign that the industry is to be pitied and that it must learn to live with radical fluctuations in sales outlook, employment, profits, and dividends to stockholders. Rather, it is a sign that it is not in control of its own markets. Other industries have used creative marketing, as well as business planning, to control these economic conditions of their lives.

Provision of Information to Customers on Industry Capabilities and Interest in Supplying Wider Segments of Their Needs

This means helping customers plan. Just as the computer manufacturers have created an enormous business in the last decade by letting their customers know they want to help them in planning to meet their business needs, so the machine tool industry can open major new business areas. In computers, for example, software today represents the single most important determinant of sales. It is in the fundamental creativity of their approach to marketing, by improving their own products and by understanding economic forces and applying them in such a way as to *create* markets for their products and services, that other industries have grown strong.

The Response to Customer Needs Through a Wider Variety of New Products

Machine tools are still replaced largely because they are worn out. Other types of equipment are frequently replaced because something better is available. All kinds of help can be obtained in developing these new products. For example, suppliers of control equipment have probably done more genuine research in machine tool problems and in manufacturing processes than have the machine tool manufacturers themselves. In the process-control industries, new suppliers of control systems are currently investing heavily in understanding the problems of end-users.

Training Salesmen

The field of numerical control has been a sorry example of how badly trained the salesmen of machine tool builders often are. It is necessary to understand the magnitude of the training it takes, particularly of sales support personnel, to create markets for newer technologies.

Innovation in Marketing Conventions

Other industries have not resigned themselves to ride the wild roller-coaster of the heavy equipment cycle. In the case of IBM and Xerox, leasing has accomplished the result. Leasing has been tried in the machine tool industry but has been largely unsuccessful, not so much because of the cost in money—the reason generally advanced—but rather because products that were offered for leasing were not sufficiently *better*. Leasing should not be looked to as a way to sell tools that cannot be sold. As T. E. Shea, vice-president of Western Electric, has suggested: "We want to come up with things that are ten times as good, so good that you can justify retiring unamortized capital equipment in order to use the new process."

The Kearney and Trecker cash-flow approach is an excellent example of what can be done through genuine understanding of customer needs—not only machine needs but financial requirements—and linking these with the realities of tax laws and the seller's own abilities to finance sales. It is in this area that other industries are creating major new markets for high technology products.

Study of Markets in Depth

The figures behind the figures must be evaluated. It is not sufficient to be content with the figures for U.S. purchases of certain kinds of machine tools. The customer's needs must be analyzed and questions must be asked with regard to what the industry could supply him with.

A decade or so ago, we passed a period of several years when European competitors were unable to deliver. This was reflected in an abnormally large volume of export business. How many took advantage of this unique opportunity to establish themselves abroad? A few, but all too few. How many established branch plants in the Common Market? How many increased their marketing efforts abroad and took the opportunity to discover the unique needs of customers in different parts of the world?

By late in the 1960's, machine tool imports rose substantially. Very frequently, this rise in imports has not been the result of "cheap" foreign labor. In most cases, it appears to have been simply a case of superior quality, workmanship, and design—often at an equal or a higher price. Foreign manufacturers are serving the needs of U.S. customers. They have evaluated the market.

Service to the Customer

Very pertinent to the above, but really a point important enough for separate treatment, is the matter of just plain service or customer relations. The point was made somewhat angrily in a recent letter to me by a machine tool industry customer:

> The last two years, have for me been an unending series of minor frustrations resulting from my dealings with the machine tool industry. They lie about delivery dates, produce misleading quotations, deliberately misinterpret specifications in their favor, refuse to acknowledge obvious errors, try to charge extra for standard features and options, ignore you when you need information, send erroneous foundation drawings, send incompetent technicians to install their machines, shortchange the distributor on whom the customer depends on maintenance during the warranty period, disconnect all their telephone lines after 5 o'clock and on weekends, which, as everyone knows, is the time machines breakdown, and then complain bitterly when you buy an imported machine. Problems do not seem to be a function of size. We have just flatly rejected two machines from [a major firm that] should know what they are doing, if anyone does. On the other hand, we have spent two months trying to install and get running a machine from . . . a pretty small company, and I am right now in the throes

> of a battle with [another firm] about a lathe that was promised to be turning out parts a month ago. All I can say is a plague on all their houses. Our biggest machine will be imported, a $400,000 machine from . . . Germany. I am keeping my fingers crossed, hoping that they will perform better than their domestic brethren. There is some hope of this since they have committed themselves to a contract that includes rather stiff economic penalties if they do not deliver on time, or if the machine does not perform to guarantees. This type of contract, by the way, is virtually impossible to get from a domestic builder.

This letter is not pleasant reading. But it describes conditions of which even firms of the most reputable character in an industry with a great tradition should be aware. Particularly, such awareness is necessary for an industry that has not only import competition but also competition from its own customers—customers who can and do produce what they cannot get from the industry.

The Study of Changes in the Customer's Organization

The emergence of the manufacturing-engineering function is symptomatic of the change that has taken place in the way customers buy machine tools. This development demands serious study in terms of selling capabilities rather than just machines for use in production. Manufacturing capabilities is what the customer really buys. The customer does not care whether he buys a lathe or a punch press; he just wants to produce his parts the best way possible.

This strategy should include analysis of market information linked with the entrepreneurial innovations already discussed. In this way, it is possible to become master of one's industry and markets and not slave to a cycle.

But, again, most important is selling the ability to produce. If not, the industry will become an ancillary, providing peripheral equipment to the industries that really supply customer needs.

TECHNOLOGICAL INNOVATIONS

Although the need for technological innovations is more widely appreciated, what passes for research and development in the machine tool industry is often only the testing of design changes. One must ask these questions:

- How much genuine research is performed in the industry and how do research-and-development expenditures as per cent of sales compare to expenditures in competitive industries?
- How many true innovations have come out of the machine tool industry in the past twenty years?
- Who does metal-working research?
- Where does the industry stand on automation?

Some of the answers to these questions may be surprising.

Genuine Research Performed in the Machine Tool Industry

Technology is changing far more rapidly than any of us realize. In 1940, the United States spent $280 million on research and development. By 1956, it had increased to $6.5 billion; it is now passing $25 billion.

A 1968 National Science Foundation report indicated that R&D expenditure for *all* manufacturing industries in 1965 was 4.3 per cent of sales. Of particular interest is that for machinery it was 4.1 per cent, for professional and scientific instruments 6.1 per cent, and for electrical equipment and communications 9.5 per cent. Percentages were slightly lower in 1966, wholly as the result of huge increases in sales. Of the *genuine* research done by the machine tool industry itself, as a per cent of sales, estimates range from a high of 3.6 per cent to a low of 2 per cent. This is a broad range, but even the high figure is low when one measures the machine tool industry's R&D, as a per cent of sales, against other industries.

There is a reluctance to commit too much money to R&D. This is understandable in view of the losses suffered in developing numerical control. However, research risks must be taken. Even research that fails to produce the desired result is often worth while. As Charles Kettering once said, "At least you have learned what doesn't work."

True Innovations Within the Machine Tool Industry over the Past Twenty Years

It is all too easy to say that there were few, if any, innovations. Of the six most important developments influencing metal-working since World War II, only one (shear spinning) originated with the machine tool industry. Of the other five, only two were developed to any extent by machine tool companies. Numerical control, electron beam, high-energy-rate forming, electric-chemical machining, and electrical-discharge machining were all developed outside the machine tool industry. Numerical control and electrical-discharge machining are the only two innovations in whose development the machine tool industry has even participated—and this after the innovation itself. The technological developments that affect the industry's business originated outside.

We live in an era of incredible technological and

business change. The first computer was built in 1945. Production models arrived about 1950. Three years later, the first computers were put to work in business, and then only over the most incredible protests. By 1969, there were 56,000 computers in the United States alone. But among the top 100 U.S. corporate users of computer systems, there is not one machine tool manufacturer. Indeed, such developments may seem remote from manufacturing, confined to an insurance company or a bank. Yet they are radically changing the entire basis for manufacturing, both in hard goods and in continuous-process manufacturing.

As Hamilton Hermon, vice-president for research and development at American Machine and Foundry, has said, "The machine of tomorrow will have to fit into a system and it will be 50 per cent electronic brain." What has this to do with innovation in the machine tool industry? It necessitates innovation, for the technology that will build these new machines will affect the process as well as the organization and conduct of manufacturing. The laser is one of the most significant potential developments for the metal-working industry. But it would be hard to find a good number of machine tool manufacturers who are even considering this device, except as a measuring tool for establishing and checking machine tool alignment.

Where Metalworking Research Is Being Done

A surprising amount of metal-working research is done in this country by firms and organizations outside the industry. Its biggest customers come first, particularly those in our space industry. The supplier companies—for example, the manufacturers of tools and tool materials—do a good deal of research. It is significant, for example, that when GE's Carboloy Division needed a high-speed lathe on which to test ceramic tooling and could not find a standard model fast or powerful enough, they had one especially designed to meet their specifications.

Because growing machine tool imports have caused industry representatives to go to Washington to seek some means of protection, it is significant to note the aggressive research into fundamental machine tool characteristics being done in Germany, particularly by Professor Opitz at Aachen. Perhaps that would be a better place to seek help than in Washington.

Where the Industry Stands on Automation

If less time were spent in pointing out the year in which the industry first made highly automatic machine tools, and more time were spent in looking at the realities of the way in which other industries are encroaching on its markets, the following would become apparent:

1. In numerical machine tool control, there is progress, as already indicated. At the Chicago Machine Tool Show in 1955, three numerical control (NC) systems were on display and in use on two types of machines. At the next show in 1960, there were about 40 NC systems in use on about 80 tools. And since then there has really been dramatic progress. Actually, some 14,000 NC's are now installed. By 1975, it is estimated that they will represent 75 per cent of the value of machine tool shipments. But there are problems as well. For example, radically new electronic techniques have been applied in most cases to machines designed for manual or mechanical control—hardly the most fruitful avenue.

2. There seems to be a tendency to put electrical cycling controls on a conventional machine and to call the result automation. In so doing, conscience is appeased and advertising and promotional possibilities are exploited. But this goes only a small way toward helping customers meet their needs.

3. The industry makes much noise about automatic screw machines, transfer machines, and special indexing machines, but actually this has not evolved much in the past ten years. Significantly, new companies have entered the field to provide the highly integrated transfer and Detroit-type automation systems.

4. There are a number of basic automation building blocks on the market. Dial tables, pallet index machines, automatic feeders, robot transfers, and so on, few made by the machine tool industry itself. One cannot but feel that in many cases users of this equipment would be far better off if these systems and devices had been manufactured by machine tool industry companies, since they know better than anyone else the requirements of perfected machine design.

What are the reasons for this lack of R&D? Is the industry really so poor and so small? To begin with, the industry as a whole readily admits that, when times are good, machine tool companies see no need for genuine R&D; when times are hard, they cannot afford it. There is a failure to see what has become apparent to almost every other major industry—that the future health of any company or industry is dependent upon the wisdom and extent of current efforts to develop new products, services, techniques, and technologies and to apply these to improving present products. Also, of course, the industry is fragmented into small companies, most of which cannot afford to undertake large R&D expenditures alone. But the industry as a whole could do so.

As a result of the limited manner in which the industry has defined itself as builders of metal cutting and forming tools, its work has not involved to any real extent the high-technology areas in which innovation is so rapidly changing its customers' needs.

The study of user needs underlying both the entrepreneurial innovations and the managerial and other marketing innovations is equally important to technological innovation. The industry must consider what can be done in manufacturing, not what its tools do. It must think in terms of providing services as well as capabilities for manufacturing, not just pieces of hardware.

THE KEY TO PROSPERITY

Prosperity for the machine tool industry—as for almost any other industry—lies in innovation: in entrepreneurial innovation and a new definition of the business; in managerial innovation or the way in which its companies are organized and its products are marketed in technological innovation and a new emphasis on the extent and kind of research and development.

Without such innovation, customers and suppliers will continue to grow more sophisticated and more independent. The industry will be headed toward a minor ancillary position in the forward march of American industry. It will be hit harder by increasingly tough and increasingly intelligent competition. Like it or not, the technological changes are here; more are coming. What can be done about it? Five specific steps might be helpful.

Research in Business Planning

The machine tool builders could undertake a program for the study of factors affecting their industry. This program might consist of these basic elements: the development of fundamental planning information; the active study of customers and their needs and the way in which they are currently satisfying these needs and a new look at technology—the technology of other industries as well as that of machine tools.

An important step has been taken already in establishing a research center for metal-cutting. This is of enormous importance, and the efforts being made by the Commerce Department and the National Machine Tool Builders Association in this direction are laudable. But to stop here is to stop too short. Business planning must guide research. In particular, there is a need for business planning that insures that the industry's environment will be receptive to technological innovation.

It is good to remember the battle over NC. There are myriad pitfalls surrounding NC control, yet it is here and it is growing. Some of the pitfalls consist of justification of the cost, maintenance of the control system, part-programming, and proper selection of machine and system. But the industry will get no place until it views these problems in perspective. NC is here, and electronic control is here, and they are going to play an increasingly important role in the future. While the problem is to overcome these pitfalls and to help customers avoid them, the industry's special problem is one of perspective.

Information from Government and Industry

This information can be applied aggressively in the design of products that answer customers' needs. The late Mr. Bannow did this when he built the Bridgeport Machine Tool Company. He owned one of the few companies that had continuous line production and that was organized in the way the industry's customers have organized their businesses. It is necessary to pioneer in the design of truly advanced machines. A creatively designed product is one of the best cures for an industry's problems.

Development of Capabilities to Attract R&D Contracts in Related Technologies

Such capabilities can be fostered either by building up internal staff or by acquiring small "applied science" companies. The U.S. Department of Defense, which supports much of the R&D of the industry's competitors, frequently funds programs that promise to improve the productivity of military hardware. Properly planned, fallout from this type of work can be very valuable as a basis for new types of machine tools. High-energy-rate forming is a direct outgrowth of this type of program.

Study of the Impact of New Technologies on Future Manufacturing

This study might begin with an analysis of the state of the art in metal-working and should include:

- Developments that influence the use of industry products
- Trends in materials use
- Analysis of the types of products major customers will be making in the future

- Technological developments that customers can use in the design of their products (controls, computers, and new processing techniques both for metals and for other materials)

Investigation of Business Opportunities

The possibility of acquiring small companies for advanced technology has been mentioned. Joint ventures and other forms of business enterprise are possible. Some of the industry's companies are also diversifying successfully. Warner & Swasey, Sundstrand, and Excello are good examples of the kind of results intelligent diversification can yield. Joint ventures are equally interesting in terms of the export market. Overseas markets are changing. There is a lot to be learned from the way in which other countries are attacking the same problems that the industry faces. It is necessary to make obsolete one's own fine products—not to allow others to do so through the back door. Plants should be designed as models of what manufacturing capabilities can be. Customers must be talked with, not only to sell machines but to gain new information on what is happening, and suppliers must be talked with as well. Corporate windows must be washed for a good look outside. And, again, above all, the industry's business must be defined in terms of new markets.

The machine tool industry laid the foundations of our industrial growth. It created the tools that enabled us to win two major and many minor wars. But only through far-sighted planning and pioneering innovation can a continuing major role built upon this foundation be assured. Business decision-making within the industry must reflect these needs. *What* the industry does with technology in an environment changed by technology will determine its future.

Chapter 7

TAKING A HARD LOOK AT HOW YOU DEFINE YOUR BUSINESS: A CASE STUDY OF THE PETROLEUM INDUSTRY

The petroleum industry has an unsurpassed record of early installation of computers, use of operations-research techniques, and computer-communications devices. It has been a leader.

The industry has a history of defining its business to serve markets created by technological change. For example, its largest single product is now gasoline to serve the age of the automobile, while at the turn of the century it was kerosene for illumination. A continuing redefinition is taking place to provide a wide range of energy products and petroleum derivatives such as synthetics.

To remain competitive and in the lead, this industry must continue to apply the new technologies in innovative ways. A continuing program to study the possibilities of infor-

mation and related technologies in the context of industry needs and the development of new concepts of petroleum marketing on the basis of the considerable investments already made in this area are among the requirements of the future. The petroleum industry has experienced change continuously in its short history. It too faces the entrepreneurial task of applying the challenge of the new technologies in ever more creative ways.

This chapter is based on an address before the American Petroleum Institute in Chicago, Illinois, November 11, 1963, as well as on an article originally published in the May 19, 1964, issue of Printer's Ink.

One thing, at least, is evident from the preceding chapters. New technologies have begun to have a pervasive impact on our entire society. This is especially so of information and related technologies. If this fact is to be fully understood and used to advantage, it must be considered in relation to the basic management of industries as a whole.

Because of the nature of the petroleum industry's operations and the traditional technical orientation of its management, it has been among the first of the American industries to use information technologies fruitfully. Its record of early installation of computers, and use of operations-research techniques and computer and communications devices is unsurpassed.

But information technologies, their products, the new families of machines, and the uses to which they are put are all changing. To remain a leader in their use and to continue to reap their benefits will take a great deal of original thinking and hard work. The nature of these upcoming changes in the petroleum industry—what they are, what their effect will be, what they mean, and what can be done about them—is the subject of this chapter.

Information and related technologies, which are, in essence, the science of extracting meaning from information and using it to control physical and managerial operations, have triggered profound changes in all aspects of our life, all related to the scientific revolution of this century. Involved are changes in the way we educate our children, run our businesses, employ other technologies, and conduct our relations with each other—changes in the very way we live.

The nature of the changes taking place is only partially reflected in the electronic computers we have come to rely upon. The computers are actually the product of a more fundamental technological development emanating from information and cybernetic theory. They are but one—albeit the first and currently most numerous—new family of machines to grow from this development. But even these machines must be viewed in the context of the proliferation of other technologies, of how they interact with these other technologies.

In other words, to properly ascertain the shape of the future, even a decade ahead, we must indeed look to the underlying technology and theory of information but also to our needs in processing, communicating, and using information in every aspect of society and life. Fundamental change is taking place through a newly found ability to build information systems to meet man's true needs. These needs are determined by technologies other than those related only to information. This means that the information technologies should not be used simply to solve yesterday's problems with tomorrow's tools.

As the theoretical concepts of cybernetics and related work take the form of commercially available systems—one of the great developments of the past decade and the next—the world of both the consumer and the manager is changing dramatically. It is the implication of this change for petroleum management to which this case study is addressed.

Even the crude precursors of the new technologies that are represented by today's information-technology developments—computer-controlled graphic displays, image storage and retrieval, data links—make clear much of what these new technologies mean to management. They offer simultaneously a challenge and an opportunity. The challenge to management is to understand the capabilities and potential of these tools and to define just what should be done with them. The opportunity is to create an entirely new level of management control through better business-information systems and to pioneer in entirely new businesses and services related to the demands of a changing society.

A HISTORICAL PERSPECTIVE

Petroleum has grown in 100 years from a gleam in Edwin Drake's eye to represent, together with related industries, about 10 per cent of the United States GNP. In that time, the prime use of petroleum products has changed almost completely from that of the nation's chief source of illumination to that of our chief source of energy.

Such is the dynamic nature of this business. Change is certainly nothing new. The industry has had a colorful history, created by bold personalities: enterprising resolute businessmen with vision. It has a proud tradition of inventive application of technology to business, leading rather than following other industries.

Everyday familiarity frequently causes us to forget just how revolutionary were the innovations of men like Drake, who had the boldness to dig for oil rather than be content to skim it off the tops of pools; John Carll, first of the petroleum geologists, who had the vision and determination to collect and correlate well records and observations and scientifically establish the nature of oil deposits while other drillers were using divining rods;

Samuel Van Sickel, who had the ingenuity to devise the first pipeline and the courage to lay it and operate it in the face of strong opposition from the railroads and truckers; and John Rockefeller, who had the enterprise to join with his competitors to stabilize the industry and organize it in corporate form. These men made the industry. And its present leaders have shown the same combination of business enterprise, technological vision, and personal boldness.

ADVANCED COMPUTER INSTALLATIONS AND APPLICATIONS

Where, then, does the industry stand today in regard to information and related technologies? They offer the tools with which to shape the future. Is the industry using them to advantage, as geology and chemistry did in the past? The answer is yes. The industry is applying information and related technologies to reduce costs, both directly by automating operations and indirectly by optimizing them. Its individual companies make important use of these new technologies. Here are some examples.

In a 1968 survey of companies ranked by the value of computer installations, 17 of 100 top companies were in the petroleum business. And even more remarkable is the fact that only 7 of those top 17 were in the top 17 by size of their sales; the other 10 ranged from 35th to 143rd in sales!

In planning, the industry is developing economic simulations such as product-profitability models, which generate optimum product mixes to maximize profits, and capital investment models, which do the same thing for capital investments.

In business operations, companies are systematically mechanizing accounting, billing, and tax reporting functions. They are making a good start in the area of uniform reporting systems, with business data being reported in standardized and codified form permitting machine manipulation, and reduction and summarization of the data for management functions.

In production, companies are putting refineries under automatic control, through the use of process-monitoring systems. They are scheduling refinery operations and developing bulk-inventory data on a daily basis through the use of digital computers. Computer programs perform the engineering calculations in bit design and use and prepare complete, optimized well-drilling programs.

In transportation there is a 1,000-mile 14-station pipeline from Texas to Ohio whose operation is completely controlled by one man sitting at a console in Longview.

In research and development, the industry is applying data processing and informational techniques to a wide variety of problems, from product-evaluation to investigation of radiation effects on hydrocarbons.

This is a proud record of accomplishment in the application of technologies that are little more than two decades old. Is this the pattern of the future? Are we going to see information and related technologies applied in the same step-by-step manner to more and more of the industry's current operations? It seems most likely that these technologies will play an ever increasing role in the petroleum industry. But the most important use of information and related technologies will take a different form. The nature of the role and manner of application will differ substantially from the piecemeal approach used to date. This difference is an important one.

We have come to the end of the first phase of the development of these new technologies and are beginning the main journey, which involves not only performing peripheral or obvious tasks but also using information to play a vital role in the mainstream of management. Information and related technologies in their brief life have had a development roughly analogous to that of a machine that has been significant in the development of the petroleum industry—the automobile. For the several years of its infancy, the horseless carriage was designed and used as just that—a horse-drawn carriage *sans* horse—even to the inclusion of the whipholder! When we in the information field look at it objectively, we can see the same pattern in our own development. Applications at first were chiefly concerned with the mechanization of specific, well-defined functions or operations that had previously been performed or controlled manually and in which the mechanization had been implemented without any significant change in the function or operation itself. But information and related technologies are changing; they are growing up. Just as the automobile evolved from a horseless carriage to a functionally designed, self-propelled vehicle, these new technologies are evolving from a cheaper (or better) way of performing existing tasks into a science of using information to achieve a fundamental objective.

As we have seen, these technologies have already had an effect on the petroleum industry. But the development of the methodology of information usage will result in its having a much deeper impact in the future. One can expect two prominent changes in the industry that are closely related to this development. They have already begun: The first is a managerial transformation leading not only to vastly more effective managerial control but, inevitably, to substantial changes in the role of many managers and, thus, the organizational structure of individual companies. The second is a change in the industry's basic orientations leading to new products and new markets and more control of both from within rather than without the industry.

Each will result in significant impacts on business decision-making in the industry. This decision-making will continue to affect *how* the companies operate but, more important by far, *what* they do in a changing environment of new markets and new competition.

MANAGERIAL CHANGES

Managerial changes are inevitable in the petroleum industry, partly because of the cost-earnings squeeze that has manifested itself in the past years. Present predictions are that the industry will keep roughly in step with the GNP in the immediate future—that is, will grow at a rate of about 4 per cent per year. Some earnings-deterioration could have been caused by operating costs increasing faster than revenues. Nonetheless, the historical price pattern of the industry is impressive. Its most important single product, gasoline, rose less than 2 per cent in service-station price between 1957 and 1967, while the national consumer-price-index rose some 19 per cent—nearly 10 times as much—over the same period. There can be little doubt that this has been accomplished largely through research leading to the aggressive application of technological improvements, including information technologies.

An interesting correlation between price stability in petroleum products and general research and development expenditures is provided by a recent National Science Foundation report.* During the mid-1960's, the petroleum industry placed sixth out of 17 major industry groups in R&D expenditures. However, over the preceding decade, the 140 per cent *increase* in these expenditures by the petroleum industry was equalled only by one other industry (aircraft and missiles) and exceeded only by the broad grouping called "nonmanufacturing industries."

If price performance in an era of rising wages and other costs can be assumed to have a direct relation to R&D efforts, with some time lag, we have here a very significant set of statistics. This is so especially when seen in the light of the leading position of petroleum companies in the use of information systems, cited above, and their increasing capital expenditures on marketing, mentioned near the end of the chapter.

The Immediacy of Changes in Management-Information Systems

In terms of computer applications, we are not speaking here about the incremental improvements obtained by automating recordkeeping. Involved is the concept of integrated management information and intelligence systems, in which a central processor participates actively in

---

**Basic Research, Applied Research, and Development in Industry,* National Science Foundation, NSF 67-12.

the day-to-day management of the company and in which a whole family of high-capacity communications media effectively put the entire company at management's fingertips. The industry's record in this score augurs well for its future.

As the informational techniques necessary to implement this management system are developed, an increasingly intimate partnership is growing between the information scientist and the business executive, with each science evolving in response to stimuli from the other. The awareness of the petroleum industry as to the requirements and advantages of this relationship is something that I can cite from my own first-hand experience. Three of its companies have been participating sponsors in a research program that my firm has been conducting in precisely this area. Preliminary study by this group of technological and software developments for the decade ahead, and their consequences in terms of today's planning and decisions, has already begun to delineate the general characteristics of future management information systems. The four most significant for the petroleum industry are as follows.

Communications

Managers will have the ability to make visual as well as aural contact with their subordinates and with their customers by means of integrated telephone-TV devices, combined with increased use of microwave equipment, and the introduction of broad-band laser trunk lines, multiplexing, and data-compression techniques. Even now, processing equipment is beginning to be more and more a direct extension of the manager through dramatic improvements in man-machine communications devices, such as dial-up data communications, high-speed page-reading, and facsimile transmission, voice input devices, and the new processing techniques of natural-language querying and image-processing.

Integration of Business and Scientific Computing

The distinction between business and scientific computers will gradually disappear. Large-scale information-processing systems of the future will be centralized facilities possessing equal proficiency in scientific and business problems. This will occur because the same computing techniques are being called for in both types of problems.

As operations research and related techniques develop, business problems are more and more concerned with arithmetic operations, linear programming, and mathematical modeling. Scientific problems are similarly involved with the data manipulation and transfer operations used in the stochastic and probabilistic analyses of physical phenomena and manufacturing processes. The integration of functions will become possible through the development of high-capacity high-speed processors, adaptive programming techniques, and comprehensive executive control systems with several input-output devices using crossbar switching networks.

Information Retrieval

Managers are beginning to have the ability to retrieve any information, textual or graphic, from the files of the largest organization within seconds. This capability results from several technical advances now emerging from the development stage: image data processing, natural-language query systems, powerful and flexible desk-top display devices, automatic document-indexing, and associative-memory techniques.

Analysis of Decision Alternatives

Managers will have available situation models for the analysis of alternative courses of action far more sophisticated than those available today. Rather than isolating and treating independently specific situations, these models will handle complex, multidimensional interactions of situations within the company and of the company with its external environment.

Scheduling, process-monitoring, capital investment, marketing, and distribution will all be simulated as the interacting operations that, of course, they are. The advances in understanding economic phenomena and in simulation techniques, as well as the developments of very high-speed low-cost computers, and new processing approaches (list structures, associative addressing) will make this possible.

These are but a few of the more immediate technical advances in information and related technologies. Heuristic, or goal-oriented systems, automatic language-translation, machines actuated by the human voice—these and many more are already in the laboratory. The capabilities they offer also will have a deep impact on management operations.

Organizational Implications

Management's span of control over personnel and operations can be greatly extended. Through advances in communications, lines of control can be tightened. Top management can be much more intimately in contact with worldwide operations and with customers. Thus, the level of control in decision-making is steadily moving to higher levels in the corporate structure.

Through this extension of control and changed information systems, management organization and duties change. Less time is needed to monitor subordinates' performance. More is available for planning. The time consumed in reviewing reports that filter up from lower levels can be decreased because managers can have instantly available to them refined data, "intelligence," at any desired level of detail.

Further, the availability of sophisticated economic models will permit the executive to plan business strategy. The making of management decisions at the strategic and policy levels will be quite different from what it is today. Much more of the pertinent data, including government statistics, and the means of reducing and summarizing them will be available. Processors will permit the analysis of all plausible alternatives to reach a decision. But creative judgment will not be replaced; on the contrary, it will become an even more important commodity because the effectiveness of its application will be dramatically improved. When we can get answers to "what would happen if" questions, we are going to feel a new heavy burden—asking the right questions.

As is discussed in the first section of this book, these technical changes are having a deep effect on the very nature of management operations and on the form of corporate organization. Operational dividing lines are crossed, bypassed, and even eliminated, because the new technologies demonstrate that division of labor and separation of function not only do not have the validity they had for manually operated systems but, more often than not, are impediments.

Information and related technologies will complete the the job of integrating the petroleum industry's companies —a task that was started by combining production, refining, transportation, and marketing under one corporate roof. This will occur through integration of the management functions of information review, decision, and operation. Already the traditional lines of demarcation between staff functions are starting to fade; administration, engineering, and operations are beginning to merge.

Because of the power of these technological tools, each man's management capability is enhanced. Fewer managers may be required, but their abilities will be more important. This represents perhaps the greatest problem posed by the management revolution: *the development of executives with the breadth to comprehend and manage corporate-wide operations and the creativity to exploit the tools provided by information and related technologies.* These men at the same time must have the judgment to adapt the corporate organization to this change.

The first task is to ascertain what we need in the way of intelligence systems. The very best men must ride herd on this question and on the transition to ensure that it is a smooth evolution rather than a convulsive upheaval.

PRODUCT AND MARKETING CHANGES

The second major change in the petroleum industry is in its basic orientation in respect to products and markets.

Redefinition of the Business

This is not a new experience for the oil business. In the last seventy years, we have seen kerosene, which represented 56 per cent of its product output in 1900, fall to 5 per cent, and gasoline, which initially was discarded as an undesirable by-product, rise to be its most important single product, representing some 45 per cent of the total market.

Gasoline and fuel oil, which now account for over 80 per cent of the petroleum market, are not in any immediate danger of being replaced; nevertheless, it is clear that the prime uses of petroleum—motive power, electric-power generation, fuel—are all undergoing fundamental changes. Some of these are already under development; others are yet to be conceived, and their nature cannot be predicted.

But, in the age where many a man born before the invention of the automobile has seen human beings on the moon, we can be certain that these changes will occur faster than they ever have before. And, when they break, their impact will be explosive. The industry will not have sixty years to adapt to the next product change as extensive as that brought about by the internal-combustion engine. The day after the nuclear-power tanker is economically profitable, it will be obsolete as a carrier of bunker oil and of other currently used petroleum fuel products.

The petroleum industry is the only sector of American industry that is concerned with the use of petroleum products. The industry itself must take action to insure that, when the needs for present products fade, it has new ones to take their place. And, because of the accelerated rate of technological change, product and market development must lead rather than follow requirements.

The shift in the conception of the industry from *product orientation to use orientation* will accelerate. Examples of this reorientation are already beginning to emerge. Industry leaders are beginning to think of themselves as suppliers of energy rather than as marketers of petroleum; witness the fact that Humble uses as its advertising slogan "America's leading *energy company!*"

Research, assisted by information technology, will be directed toward the creation of new energy uses for petroleum. Promising developments are the replacement of coke by oil in the hydrocarbon injection method of making steel and the conversion of fossil energy to electricity by the fuel cell. Others will emerge from the research laboratories.

At the same time, the petroleum industry will begin to broaden its horizons in another dimension—the conception of the very products it markets. It is likely that the industry will start to think of itself as marketer of hydrocarbon products.

The manufacture of petrochemicals, which originated in the desire to obtain some revenue from the unavoidable by-products of petroleum-refining, presently accounts for only 2 per cent of the petroleum industry's output, but it has grown some twenty-four times in the last two decades to an annual production of 60 billion pounds. It now supplies about 80 per cent of all the organic chemicals used in the United States.

Petroleum has little competition in its value as a source of hydrocarbons. The surface has just been scratched.

Professor Frederick Rossini at the Carnegie Institute of Technology has reported that only 169 of a probable 1 million petroleum hydrocarbons have been fully identified.

Petroleum industry research laboratories, using advanced information-processing techniques to systematize their data and mathematical compound models for analysis and synthesis, will be the source of organic materials that will surpass the utility and profitability of some of the more spectacular developments of the past, such as butyl rubbers, synthetic fibers, detergents, and plastics.

The nature of the petroleum industry and petroleum products is changing. The industry must define clearly the nature of its business in terms consistent with future markets and products. As the preceding chapter indicates, this is far from being a simple matter.

New Marketing Strategies and Goals

In its emerging role as supplier of energy and creator and marketer of hydrocarbons, the industry will undergo a revolution in its approach to marketing. Its marketing objectives will be redefined. Instead of merely working to expand the markets for the industry's existing products, petroleum marketers will work to analyze consumer needs and translate these into requirements for new products. They will work hand in hand with researchers to develop these products and then, only then, will they create and cultivate markets.

With the time compression implicit in today's technological growth, it is no longer possible to afford the luxury of waiting for the market to demand the product. It is necessary to anticipate the requirements and have the products ready and, frequently, assist in creating the markets. More control of products and markets must be held within the industry itself, if it is to flourish in the future as in the past.

Information and communications technologies will play a vital role in this aspect of tomorrow's petroleum industry. They never were and never will be a substitute for either scientific or entrepreneurial creativity. But they provide the means to implement the products and aid the process of such creativity more effectively and rapidly than has ever been possible before. They will not be the raw material but rather the catalyst of petroleum's new products and markets.

The techniques of data processing, information retrieval, and sophisticated correlation methods, coupled with scientific analysis methods, will find use in the identification and classification of hydrocarbon compounds. And advanced information techniques, perhaps to be developed by researchers in the petroleum industry itself, will provide more realistic economic and industrial models for analysis of markets and product requirements.

THE REQUIREMENTS OF THE FUTURE

The petroleum industry has experienced change continuously in its relatively short life and, in fact, has been in the forefront of most industries in adapting to change. The future will bring changes at least as far-reaching as any in the past. These changes will occur principally in the areas outlined above—management operations and product and market orientation—and the industry will be using information and communications technologies extensively to shape and control these changes to its advantage.

It must be remembered, however, that there is nothing magic about automation. Automated systems do only what they are told to do. Their limitations are the user's limitations; their effectiveness will be in proportion to the user's ingenuity in applying them.

A Planning Program

It is possible to offer suggestions for a planning program that will help to insure the readiness of the industry to greet technological changes as opportunities to reduce costs and increase revenues, rather than as threats to its present operations. For example, it may be useful to conduct a three-point research program to develop applications of information and communications technologies, in their broadest sense, to the problems of petroleum-industry management. Its elements might include:

1. *Investigation of the needs of petroleum management for data and business intelligence.* This would be done in the context of the systems made possible by these technologies in the next decade. It would involve taking a fresh look at management operations: studying data requirements critically and objectively to determine precisely what management needs and when. The application of information techniques and tools to the problems of business management, as well as to the problems of scientific research, requires an investment that is not small, but the return will more than justify it.

As has been pointed out in previous chapters, it is necessary to place the highest caliber of line managers in charge of this work—managers who understand the petroleum industry as businessmen, men who have the imagination to understand and exploit the potential of information and communications technologies in virgin territory and do so in business terms.

Such a study should be directed at top corporate management—not within the confines of finance, records management, or the like. The view must be company-wide or the effort will fail. It also must be in terms of the most advanced aspects of these technologies, for it is only here that one can properly understand the direction in which we are so rapidly moving.

2. *Provision for a continuing program.* The new tools are not to be handed to any of us full blown; new devices, new techniques, new procedures, are appearing continually. Therefore, it is necessary to develop an orderly program of interim steps toward the future management system.

Each development requires evaluation to determine whether its use would be consistent with the system goal. In particular, the man-machine and machine-machine interface is worthy of analysis. It does not suffice to be content with the use of powerful new communications media to hook up existing computer facilities; conversely, powerful new processors should not be confined with the relatively low-level capability of existing peripheral devices.

And, as machine systems evolve, it is essential to develop the management procedures and organizational modifications to exploit them.

3. *Development of a new concept of petroleum marketing.* Too often in the past, petroleum marketing has been limited to the study of service-station problems and

predictions of the number of new motor-vehicle registrations and driver-license applications each year. Perhaps the principal point of this chapter revolves around the increasingly evident necessity of putting some solid effort into a determination of just what role the industry has really played and can play in the future.

Already the industry has begun to look critically at present and future products and markets. Using information and related techniques as a tool, it is developing market-research methods that give better insight into customer requirements with respect to current and new products. Its capital expenditure for marketing in 1962 began to exceed expenditures for refining for the first time in the history of the industry, but it is necessary to make sure that this extensive retail-sales organization plays a really fundamental role in the future.

As a basic consideration in this new approach to marketing, it is essential to look carefully at the social implications of the changes being wrought by technology. Our way of life is changing; and this will have as much effect on product requirements, consumer patterns, and marketing approach, as will the product and market changes caused directly by technological advances.

This third aspect of the proposed research program is fundamental to the whole industry and might very well be handled by establishing a petroleum-marketing research Institute.

The petroleum industry, like many other leading industries, is approaching a period of very substantial change in nearly every aspect. This means a correspondingly varied set of challenges and opportunities. The industry has taken a leading role in the first phases of the information revolution. It is far ahead and has led much of American industry into this new age and must maintain this lead. As with any important endeavor, this will not be easy to do.

The machines that follow computers and communications devices should be greeted with the same perspicacity and receptiveness as were the major technological innovations of the past. Today's machines are only the first of many new families of machines.

Above all, the business must be viewed with fresh eyes in order to define exactly what the petroleum business is and what it can become. The task of managers is to define what is needed in relation to what the new technologies can provide. This is as much an entrepreneurial task as a technological one and, as has already been pointed out in preceding chapters, is too important to be left to the technicians.

One of the more colorful men in the petroleum industry once said, "If opportunity is seized as it comes, it doesn't have to be chased when it goes." One can go a step further. Those prepared for the opportunity when it comes will not have to catch it on the fly—they may even be able to create it.

Chapter 8
GOOD AS WELL AS BAD USE OF TECHNOLOGY: A CASE STUDY OF THE RAILROAD INDUSTRY

The railroad industry presents examples of new ways of looking at a system and of the need to do so. Railroads are systems, among the first of the industrial age; they are the culmination of technological innovations that began in steam power; and from their beginnings they have been tied to the social change and problems of the day. The decisions of the railroad industry—its potentials for success or failure—are central to the needs of a changing society.

Railroad management must provide not only a basic means of national transportation but also a domestic system of mass transportation in the space age. Some of the most advanced responses to the human problems and opportunities presented by the new technologies are to be found among the railroad systems of the world. Entrepreneurial and managerial innovations are based on a tradition of technology inherent in railroading from its beginnings.

The railroad industry can remain competitive by accepting the challenge of the new technologies. If it is not to be left behind by the preservation of existing uneconomical systems and services, it must conceive new railroad systems and organize effectively to meet the social problems with which the new technologies have presented it. Even within its regulatory constraints there is room for much improvement. But part of the job is to work toward modification of these constraints to allow meeting transportation needs as a multimode system.

This chapter is based on the opening address before the Plenary Session of the International Railway Symposium on Cybernetics, in Paris, France, November 4, 1963.

A case study of the railroad industry provides a particularly appropriate conclusion to this section of the book. First, railroads are *systems*—among the very first of the industrial age. Information and communications *systems* provide an interesting and important opportunity to project railroads into the future. In other words, a new look can be taken at the old railroad systems through the new technologies, especially through the new conceptual and analytical tools that make these new technologies into effective instruments. We now have new ways of examining not only *how* these old systems operate but *what* they do to serve the needs of *changing society.*

Second, technology is inherent in railroading. Railroads represented the culmination of technological innovations that began two or three centuries ago in steam power and precision engineering. Their operations were profoundly affected by electricity and the telegraph. What they did was expanded by technologies ranging from internal combustion to refrigeration. Also, they have fallen victim to still other technological breakthroughs, such as air and automobile transport. Thus, the decisions of railroad management must encompass not only an understanding of the possibilities of information and related technological developments but of many other technologies as well.

Third, as a result, railroads are inextricably involved in the social changes brought about by technology. This is true internally, in terms of human problems involving the need for new skills and the obsolescence of old skills. Above all, however, it is true because of the external elements, such as the growth of metropolitan areas and the demand for speedy transport over short and long distances.

Fourth, there have been both successes and failures in this industry. All facets of change have been met either poorly or well: the *how,* the *what* and the service to a revolutionized *society.* The potentials of success or failure in the decisions of the railroad industry are staggering, because these decisions are central to the needs of a changing society. Neither machine tools nor petroleum have this quality.

Finally, the railroad industry can be discussed on truly international terms. Indeed, there is a common denominator of experience and there are common problems that run through railroad industries throughout the world, whether in free-enterprise or fully planned economies, whether publicly or privately owned.

A HISTORICAL PERSPECTIVE

Near the middle of the nineteenth century, railroads crossed paths with the computer for the first time. The British mathematician Charles Babbage, intrigued by the French First Republic's project to produce mathematical tables through the use of a group of humans organized to work rather like a large computing machine and following in the footsteps of Pascal and Leibnitz, devised first his difference engine and then his analytic engine, encompassing in his designs many of the essential principles of today's electronic computer. What is less known is that, after thirty years of frustration at the inability of the artisans of his day to build his machines, he turned his attention to railroads, where he made several notable contributions by inventing the speedometer and the dynamotor car. We can only speculate at the difference in the history of both fields if he had had the tools to turn his genius to reality.

Today, we do have the tools to build virtually any machine system we wish. But can we find the men? This may be one of the key problems railway management will face in ushering in the new age of automation. We are now at a point of time when, as in almost every aspect of enterprise management, science and technology provide the opportunity for a revolutionary change in the railroads.

As is demonstrated in the preceding chapters, today's plethora of electronic machines is the first product of an onrushing stream of new technologies—information and communications technologies. The newly-found ability to build machine systems to handle and communicate information for any of man's needs is making possible an altogether new age of mass transportation.

There has been what might be called a wide "technological stirring" within the world's railroad industry, particularly since the end of World War II, leading to major increases in productivity. Thus, in many countries, we have seen extensive modernization of plant and equipment. Diesel electrification has importantly supplanted the steam locomotive as railroad motive power. Rolling stock has increased capacity, stronger and lighter-weight construction, and vastly improved running-gear, axle, and journal performance. Widespread emphasis has been placed on special-purpose freight cars and on larger tare-weight-to-loaded-weight ratios. Maintenance of way has become importantly mechanized, in the main performed by small crews with highly efficient, multipurpose power machinery. Signaling and communication developments have led to the large-scale introduction of radio and have extended use of the telegraph and, in switching and car communication, have introduced microwave and centralized traffic control and have resulted in the development of major automated freight yards. Finally, large electronic computers have begun, albeit slowly, to extend to management areas beyond accounting, payroll, inventory, and ordering procedures. However, these technological applications only begin to suggest some of the major changes that information systems can make when fully and creatively applied to railroads.

INFORMATION SYSTEMS AND RAILROAD SYSTEMS

Some of the more obvious consequences of the use of information and related technologies to railroads can be summarized here. But the problems and wider implications are discussed later in this case study. The first is effective car utilization resulting from automatic, accurate, and current freight-car inventory. Apart from required maintenance periods, scheduled automatically by the system, cars will be used for the major portion of the twenty-four hours of each day of the year, thus appreciably lowering the high inventory of car units. In the United States, for example, it is estimated that the more than 1.8 million car units are each moving for an average of only 2 hours and 40 minutes a day and cover 54 miles daily.

A second is increase in freight tons carried per train. The national averages of freight ton carried per train now range between less than 100 tons to more than 1,500 tons. Another measure of this is in freight-ton kilometers per operated kilometer of track, where the national averages now range between less than 200,000 to nearly 4 million tons per kilometer, and in freight-car ton capacity per car where the national averages now range from 10 to more than 57 tons. It will be possible to move consistently up to and beyond these figures.

A third consequence of the use of information and related technologies is reliable service and assurance of consistency of total transit time. No longer need there be long waits in yards to assemble "economic trains," waits in intermediate yards for the reclassification of trains, or any of the long delays inherent in freight terminals. Another gain is increased productivity. In the United States, averages of the number of traffic units per employee, in terms of passenger miles and freight-ton miles, range from 243,000 to over 3.6 million traffic units. Again, it will be possible to attain and exceed the upper limits of this wide range. Furthermore, the proper pricing of customer charges will be made possible by the data accumulation of precise costs and cost components of freight and passenger operations. Finally, it will be possible to effectively control a railroad system so that it will be more responsive to customer as well as national needs. The commercially relevant definition of the railroad's proper and changing role in the space age, vis-à-vis other forms of transportation, and the tools to effectively plan the realization of such a role and analyze its performance are the major channels of such an effective control capability.

The above changes can occur in railroad operation and management as a result of the application of information and related technologies, yet they are only the most obvious changes. Their application to the enterprise of railroad systems can fundamentally alter the nature of railroading, the task of railroad management, and the role of railroads in our age.

Actually, we see today only the tip of the iceberg. The bulk of the information revolution—and, therefore, its application to railroads—has yet to reveal itself fully. Already discussed in the preceding chapters are new families of machines: information storage and retrieval systems, heuristic or goal-oriented systems, and language-translation systems actuated by the spoken voice—a few examples of new machines all arising from the present technological base. Such technology is laying the ground-work of all-encompassing information systems for the centralized control of enlarged railway systems. For the first time, we can speak of the basis for the introduction of integrated information systems that will truly match the real operating and planning problems and the customer needs of today's and tomorrow's railroads.

ECONOMIC AND REGULATORY CONSTRAINTS

Along with this promise, technology holds major problems for railroad management. The difficult economic and financial position since 1945 of the railroads of most countries reflects major social and industrial changes within their economies. For example, this is evident in the rail-share percentage decrease in many countries of certain bulk traffic, as well as in the emergence and strengthening of other forms of transportation such as trucking, inland waterways, and airlines, with respect to cargo, and automobiles and airlines with respect to passengers.

Thus, railroad freight traffic, as a percentage of total

freight traffic, is in most countries declining compared with other forms of freight transportation. This importantly determines the funds available for technological applications since, with some notable exceptions, railroad passenger traffic is not profitable and railroad freight traffic generates the funds to pay for research and improvement.

Severe governmental and institutional constraints exist for railroad management in many countries and can limit the application of technology to railroad operations. This expresses itself in inequalities of governmental regulation of the railroads vis-à-vis other transportation forms: the extent of the industry regulated, the expenditure of government investment monies and subsidies, taxation, and so on, as well as, in some countries, strong resistance by trade unions to the application of technological changes.

Within the context of these problems, railroad management still has the responsibility of providing not only a basic means of national transportation but also a dynamic system of mass transportation in the space age. This opportunity—only partially technological, importantly managerial—presents a number of decisive and interrelated questions:

- How can railroad management best ensure the vision necessary to conceive of new railroad systems?
- Does railroad management recognize the new organizational and managerial implications that information and communications technologies raise when applied to railroads?

- Will railroad management properly meet the decisive human challenges involved in the application of these technologies?

THE VISION TO CONCEIVE OF NEW RAILROAD SYSTEMS

Railroads in the nineteenth century were the symbol and the product of the imaginative use of what, for its time, was an exceedingly advanced technology. Interestingly enough, they were also precursors of the systems concept.

The Systems Concept

Fundamental to the proper use of information and communications technologies is an initial conception of the scale and scope of the system. In countries such as the United States, served by a number of interconnecting railroads, or in areas such as Western Europe, it would seem necessary, when first planning the application of these new technologies, to conceive of the system as the full system of connecting railroads serving the public and to treat this as something that must be subjected to integrated control. In other words, the constraints of history must not be permitted to artificially limit service to the public in planning the use of technology. There is little justification for the duplication, cost, and loss of control resulting from separate systems for the handling of freight and passenger and car accounting by the interconnecting roads.

There also is a pressing need for coordinating investment policy on the basis of reliable and comparative cost figures and for coordinating tariffs and rates. To achieve these ends requires a railroad network integrated by an over-all system of information and control.

The movement toward railroad integration with the European Economic Community and, in a sense, the railroad-merger movement in the United States are starts in this direction. The efforts being made by the International Union of Railways for a common European solution to the problem of automatic coupling; cooperative interchange of rolling stock among Class I, line-haul railroads of the United States, Canada, and Mexico; the electrification program of most European trunk lines in relation to trans-European passenger services; and the announcement of the planned establishment of a joint fleet of railroad cars by the Soviet Union and countries of Eastern Europe, to be controlled by a central office in Prague—are all straws in this same wind.

Managerial Decisions

But the necessity for management vision implies much more than the rationalization of existing methods of doing business and of making equipment and procedures compatible, or of doing business on a more extensive geographical scale. Something akin to great entrepreneurial decisions, or insights into business definition, should be called forth if we are to effectively use the new technologies. This is not the kind of development we can predict or prescribe in detail, but we have ample historical precedent to know that proper use of such a radical new tool as information and related technologies requires radically new conceptions of the enterprise.

We too easily forget just how great were the innovations of the nineteenth century, which produced today's form of railroad. It has been said of that period that the true history of technologically advanced countries was the history of transportation in which the names of the presidents of railroads were more important than the names of the heads of state.

Systems and Social Needs

New railroad systems are necessary today. They must be based upon management understanding of both the specific conditions that can enable railroads to capitalize on their special assets, and the proper relationship of railroad transportation vis-à-vis other forms of transportation. Railroad management must persuade government and the public that they must be permitted to stop doing things that railroads are ill suited to do and, as technology permits, to do the things for which they are suited. This in itself requires extensive study. In most countries, as the recent experiences of both the International Union of Railways and the British Railways attest, there has never been a national inventory of what transportation services are needed nor a systematic, comprehensive assembly of information upon which railroad planning could be founded.

In truth, we are speaking of a process that has already begun, painfully, slowly, and unevenly, within each country—a process pointing to a coordinated development of all types of transport as components of a single, unified, transport system. It is as part of this inevitable development that railroad management is confronted with the problem of conceiving and implementing new railroad systems.

THE RECOGNITION OF NEW ORGANIZATIONAL AND MANAGERIAL IMPLICATIONS

The application of information systems to world railroads requires people intimately knowledgeable about the new technologies and imbued with the vision to apply them. It requires people who understand the necessary techniques of transition, how the technologies can be applied without the disruption and paralysis of existing functions.

Organization

A host of problems relating to organizational structures are raised. Consider, for example, the responsibility of applying the new technologies and concepts, of incorporating them into existing systems, and of putting them to work. This responsibility is usually placed at a middle-management level, either in the comptroller's or in the engineer's office. But, as in other enterprises discussed in this book, proper planning raises many questions that require far more extensive top management planning participation on the use of the new technologies than is now customary, with some notable exceptions of course.

As long as railroad computers dealt only with payrolls, interline revenues, and freight and passenger accounts and claims—essentially clerical work—they could organizationally be part of the comptroller's responsibility. However, once they begin to be applied to scheduling, rate-making, cost control, and other planning functions, computer application and responsibility require different positioning within the organization. And this is but one of many organizational problems, some quite far-reaching in their effect on organizational structure, that confront railroad management in applying these technologies to railroad operations.

Management

Once planned and installed, the implementation and use of information systems in railroads result in fundamental changes in managerial techniques. It suffices to distinguish, at this point, between two aspects of management utilization of the new technologies.

The first, and perhaps the only one that is generally considered, is the way in which management uses technology to change operating procedures and methods within the business. This is important and complex. Yet in a way, it is the smallest part of the problem, though it unfortunately too often becomes the center.

The second is the way in which management uses the new technologies, not only to change the manner in which a task is done but to determine what task should be done. Thus, an important part of management's problem is in knowing what questions to ask. This involves the ability to see a pattern emerging from changing technology, so as to introduce wholly new ways of performing basic functions and of applying technology in altogether new ways to serve user needs. Entrepreneurial flair looks to technology not simply to improve the way a job is performed but also to see whether it is possible to find an altogether different way of better fulfilling the same and, often, new and still-unperceived needs.

Until now, in railroad operation, the application of information and communications technologies has been directed to the cost of knowing (primarily accounting) and to ways of reducing that cost. In designing railway-information systems, we should be primarily concerned with the costs of *not* knowing—*not* knowing where cars are, *not* knowing what will cause specific delays and for how long, *not* knowing what kind of trouble has started, and *not* knowing where the solutions lie.

Thus, in the utilization of the new technologies and in the implementation of the systems they make possible, management is confronted with the essence of the problems of operational costs, car utilization, maintenance ratio, and parts utilization and scheduling, rather than with improving techniques to cope with the results of such problems. A new order of managerial skills, as discussed in the preceding chapters, is also required in the railroad industry.

Along with the need for new managerial skills comes the need to be alert to the possible managerial pitfalls. The mere existence of the computer in an organization and its prolific production of date too readily allow many managers to feel that they are using this new tool effectively. We must concern ourselves as much with what information we process as with new methods of processing, with what information we communicate as with new methods of communication.

Personnel

It is already apparent that central among the problems management faces in applying information systems, throughout all types of industries, is the human problem. There are two aspects to this: developing the type of people required to introduce, implement, and manage these systems and coping with the displacements resulting from technological applications.

Unless we apply to both problems an imagination equal to the technologies, the fruits of modern science cannot be utilized successfully by the railroads or by other industries. The human problems are the most crucial and at the same time the most difficult of the questions discussed here. In many ways, the human area is the area about which we know the least.

We have already observed that the kind of person required for the conception and implementation of railway-information systems must be highly creative. This is true of those responsible for technological, marketing, and above all, managerial functions; for what is required is an understanding of the technologies meshed into analytical imagination and the deepest insight into the true workings and needs of the railroad industry in this new age.

Personnel practices and management systems will have to be geared to attract and keep the imagination and skill required. Recently reported difficulties on the part of several railroads in attracting qualified personnel only emphasize that times are changing, and personnel practices of the new age must differ from those suitable to the managerial and technical structures of the past.

The human problems resulting from technological change also have a second crucial dimension that is highlighted by the nature of the times in which we live. The philosopher Alfred North Whitehead has stated one of the important facts differentiating our time from others: "the rate of progress is such that an individual human being of ordinary length of life will be called upon to face novel situations which find no parallel in his past. The fixed person for the fixed duties, who in older societies was such a godsend, in the future will be a public danger."

Pope John XXIII devoted must of his encyclical *Mater et Magistra* to the enunciation of this problem and to calling for imagination, insight, and compassion in dealing with it.

It is the problem of human displacement resulting from technological change that, for many, continues to be the most vexing. Its solution involves two facets: Management must have the freedom to introduce new technology as it becomes economically feasible. But, at the same time, it is not in the nature of our times to freely give management that prerogative, unless management is prepared to guarantee that displaced workers do not suffer as a result of the introduction of such technology. Indeed, this involves responsibility on the part of trade unions not to perpetuate unnecessary positions and archaic and outmoded staffing patterns that debase the worker rather than sustain him. However, management's responsibility to persuade unions and government of the urgent need for proposed changes is actually even greater. It includes the taking of the necessary steps to assure that the benefits of technological applications are not outweighed by the burdens of individual hardship.

In this respect the experience of the British Railways Board, partially repeated in the Netherlands, is most instructive. As early as 1957, agreement was reached with the Railway Trade Unions with regard to the manning of diesel and multiple units. Established arrangements with respect to discharge have been significantly revised so as to ameliorate displacement difficulties; a scheme for substantial resettlement payments for those permanently displaced has been negotiated; agreements have been reached on efforts to retrain the displaced and provide them with new job opportunities.

THE NEED FOR ENTREPRENEURIAL FREEDOM AND NEW CONCEPTS OF SCALE

These, then, are some of the major managerial problem areas that increasingly, and most forcefully, will engage the attention and understanding of railroad management. In order to overcome these problems and to achieve the economic benefits that are so tantalizingly near in this new age of technological innovation, certain conditions should be fulfilled.

Railroad management must have the freedom to deploy the new technologies in the way that can best serve the public. This requires a fundamental reappraisal of the many constraints placed upon railroads and railroad management. These constraints take many forms. Some are intangible, such as ideas of what properly constitutes a railroad and a railroad system and how it should behave; others are far more tangible, such as the mass of discriminatory legislative and executive regulation. There are also institutional constraints, which most railroads in the world have inherited from the past. The suggested reappraisal must take a different form in each country, for the constraints differ in each country, but the same freedom must emerge.

The scale of the new railroad-information systems should not be artificially limited by national boundaries or political ideologies. The information systems of which we are speaking allow us to parallel the real flow of freight and passengers in the new railroad systems and, thus, truly and properly serve the needs of the public.

The scale of these new systems will vary. It would seem altogether logical, for example, that the European system be one that at least encompasses all the Western and some Eastern European countries in one truly European railroad system.

Similarly, the appropriate scale in the United States would not be a separate system for each private railroad but rather a single, integrated on-line information system to serve all freight and car accounting and control for the entire United States. Neither proposal requires common ownership. But simple common sense dictates that we match the scale of the solution to the scale of the problem. Information and communications technologies allow us to do this.

It may be appropriate to establish an International Railway Institute on Information Technology that would unite railroads from every country in the world. Such an Institute would act as a clearing house, as well as focus and spur the development of the necessary climate and opportunities for the most rapid application of information systems by the world's railways.

Railroads face powerful opponents: whole industries and entrenched institutional, governmental, and labor constraints, as well as the inertia of looking at and doing things in essentially usual ways. However, the further ahead one looks, the greater becomes the public's need for railroads as a means of mass transportation. As information and communications technologies immeasurably increase interdependence between producers, consumers, and government, railroad management has the task of fashioning and implementing a picture of the railroad systems of the future—railroad systems that have a future.

Railroads have always played the oracle's role to business, government, and society as a whole. The industry started its history as the child of science capturing the imagination of an age. Railroading became the aspiration of children throughout the world, fascinating generations of their elders and playing a central role in building today's world. The birth of railroads in the first half of the nineteenth century was truly an age of science and technology applied on an epic scale. And it was perceived as such by the men who made the age.

At an industry meeting in St. Louis in 1849, Mr. James Gadsden of the South Carolina Railroad Company said:

> The poetry of mechanism is one of the most interesting departments of the poetry of science, and that of railroads cannot fail to be regarded as the *Iliad* of its productions, embracing the accounts of works, the most expensive and gigantic, the description of engines, the most ingenious and complex, and the history of social ameliorations, which are now altering the very condition of man, virtually extending the term of his existence, and opening new and extensive fields for the exercise of his holiest and noblest affections.

Today, as railroad management applies imagination and creativity on a broad scale to the aggressive utilization of new technologies and to better ways of meeting human needs for mass transportation and deals boldly and compassionately with managerial and human questions, we may begin to feel with confidence that ahead of us rather than behind us could lie the golden age of railroads. The industry can remain competitive by accepting the challenge of the new techniques. But to do so it must conceive of new railroad systems and organize effectively to meet the social problems with which the new technologies have presented it. Even regulatory constraints can be ameliorated by working toward their modification to permit the meeting of transportation needs through a multimode system.

Railroads have been able to absorb every new demand of the times on the human and industrial level. Information and communications technologies, which are on the threshold of new discoveries in these same areas, are natural partners for advanced railroad management. Ultimately, railroad systems and information systems are parallel, perhaps more so than in most industries.

PART III

Using Technological Change to Create New Opportunities for the Enterprise: Four Case Studies

Chapter 9

WHEN MONEY GROWS IN COMPUTERS: A CASE STUDY OF THE BANKING INDUSTRY

The banking industry illustrates the potential and the need for an old industry to do new things, in effect, to create new enterprises. There has been considerable confusion among the banking industry's management regarding the nature of the role of banking in the future and how this role can be filled. Powerful competition is waiting in the wings to take over the finance-related services that banking might fail to provide. Also, information and communications technologies are beginning to sap sources of banking income —for example, income from demand deposits—by enabling corporate customers to reduce their liquidity requirements. Therefore, not only must the banking industry interdict the incursions of technologically based competition, but it must find new sources of revenue. The provision of electronic money-and-credit-transfer services, as well as of financial management for corporations, smaller businesses, and individual customers, would help meet both of these requirements for continued growth.

The way banking operates has already undergone substantial change as the result of technological innovations, and what banking does in terms of new services has also changed. But, for industry to maintain its central role in the economy, more must be done to apply the new technologies to the development of new services required by a rapidly changing society.

This chapter is based on an article originally published in the November–December, 1967, issue of the Columbia Journal of World Business.

This chapter is the first of a section devoted primarily to future possibilities. Here, using the banking industry as a case study, is an example of the way in which technology can be viewed not only as a new way of performing old tasks by new procedures but as a way to cause business to do new things. The differences—and both perceptions—are important. They result from recognizing that business *policy* as well as procedural questions are often posed by technological change. The so-called cashless society is a particularly interesting example.

There are really only two startling things about the cashless society in the United States. One is that a small but important minority of bankers until recently did not think it was going to come about—or not soon, anyway. The other is that the great majority of the bankers who were expecting it neither could agree on how it would develop nor appeared willing to plan for it.

The first of these statements is borne out by a survey on the impact of electronics on money and credit,* which included a 29-point questionnaire sent to some 10,000 individuals in the United States, including more than 4,000 bank presidents and other top executives in banking. Of the respondents, 27 per cent did *not* believe that a cashless society would develop by 1977 to 1982. Even among the 100 leading banks, this view prevailed among 20 per cent.

The second statement finds support not only in the survey but in the initial chaotic reactions of a large number of bankers in credit-card and related areas of credit-and-money transfer. Some 95 per cent of the bank respondents, expecting a cashless system, believed that banks

---

*The Diebold Research Program, 1966.

would play a major role in such a system. But there was wide disagreement among them as to how it would come about—through the further development of credit cards, the expansion of automatic overdraft privileges, the automation of interbusiness transactions, or other means—and as to who, if anyone, will be the operating partners or other principal beneficiaries of an electronic system. Perhaps some sort of decision, conscious or not, is taking place. As of 1969, several thousand U.S. banks were reportedly in the credit-card field, serving more than 50 million cardholders. Many of these banks had rather highly mixed initial results in terms of profits and doubtful prospects for long-term viability in the credit-card business, although recent cooperative arrangements resulting in nationwide systems have greatly improved this outlook. A large number of banks are instituting automatic overdraft privileges and check-cashing guarantees, sometimes as an alternative to and at other times as an integral part of credit-card operations. Still, at least one of the very major banks recently was looking once again at the possibility of entering the traveler-check market—a business with a glorious past and a rather uncertain domestic future.

What happened was neither new nor unusual. A large number of businesses were getting ready to lose a great deal of money over the next decade or so. Not only banks were involved. The survey also went to several thousand leading nonbanking financial service businesses, manufacturers (including the computer industry), retailers, utilities and oil, transportation, and communications companies. Understandably, the division of opinion among these groups was even more marked than among the bankers. Their views on who will operate and benefit from an electronic system of money-and-credit transfer and whether or how it will come about lead one to suspect that the principal, potential operators of such a system have a major marketing job ahead of them, once they decide what they have to sell.

By 1969, the situation both inside and outside the banking industry had changed considerably. As indicated, nationwide credit-card systems were developing and were effectively merging the retail card with the travel and entertainment card. Also, potential users of an electronic money and credit transfer system—manufacturing and retail firms, for example—were beginning to take a serious look at its potential.

However, the main question still remains: Do the prospective operators of such a system have something worthwhile to sell? In approaching this question, three of its fundamental components can be subjected to analysis:

- What are the macro- and micro-economic factors involved?
- What are the technologies available?
- What are the most probable forms, in terms of operations and business opportunities, of a future system of electronic money-and-credit transfer?

These problems profoundly affect the future of most kinds of financial institutions. Also, they affect many other types of enterprises, ranging from retailers to utilities, to a degree directly dependent on the relative importance of financial operations to their costs of doing business. Finally, they have important implications for the manufacturers and service companies that produce, lease, or service the computer, communications, and peripheral equipment needed for an electronic money and credit transfer system.

THE CASHLESS SOCIETY

Before going into these problems, it may be helpful to take a rather broad, speculative look at what is meant by the so-called cashless society. What will our system of financial transactions consist of in, let us say, ten to fifteen years? What will it mean to the consuming public, the financial business communities, and government by 1983?

In the first place, the cashless society will not be cashless. As discussed further on, a substantial number of transactions will continue to be made as they are made today, using currency, checks, and other traditional means. Actually, the outstanding characteristics of a future system of electronic money and credit transfer will be a great reduction in paper handling of all kinds and a resulting decrease in transaction times, errors, and costs. To characterize the future system as cashless is about as accurate and meaningful as characterizing our present system as barterless. But we are more or less stuck with the term cashless society, and it is used here interchangeably with the terms automated or electronic money and credit transfer.

Consumer System

For consumers, the cashless society will mean the carrying of one or two cards with which to make cash payments or obtain credit at the time and place of purchase, or from any other location, over the telephone. One card could serve both the money-and-credit transfer functions, or there could be two cards—one for money and the other for credit. In order to prevent fraud, various types of identification procedures will be available, including photographs on the cards, signature comparison, and voice

EXHIBIT 10

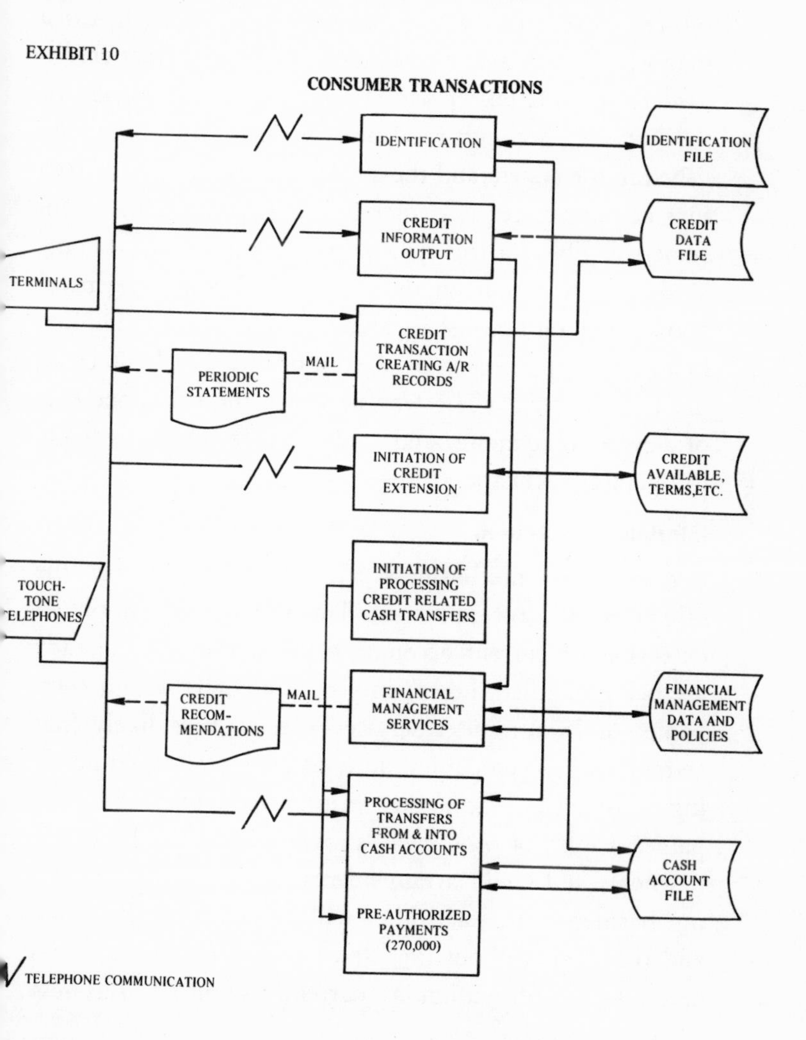

identification. Consumers will be able to transfer money from their own accounts to those of others. Or they could ask for credit through the system. Both the money transfer and the amounts and terms of credit received will depend on the money in the consumers' accounts and on their credit ratings, as recorded within the system. In addition, for a number of purchases, transactions similar to current credit-card usage will take place. That is, at the discretion of the retailer, accounts-receivable records will be established in the system and the consumers will be billed from that account at regular intervals. It is possible that consumers eligible for this type of transaction will have some kind of designation on their cards, indicating a general good credit rating, just as today such a rating is implicit in a person's possession of a retail or travel and entertainment credit card. (The way in which the consumer part of an electronic money and credit transfer system is likely to operate is illustrated in Exhibit 10.)

Interbusiness System

Automated interbusiness transactions will form the other part of a future system. This will be very simply an extension of current accounting procedures that already are being handled increasingly by computers within companies or by computer service bureaus. It is likely that certain service companies, such as computer manufacturing subsidiaries, accounting firms, communications companies, banks, or others will provide the means by which payments and credit arrangements among enterprises doing business with each other will be automatically made and recorded, without the use of papers for billing, payment, and confirmation as currently required. Business

KHIBIT 11

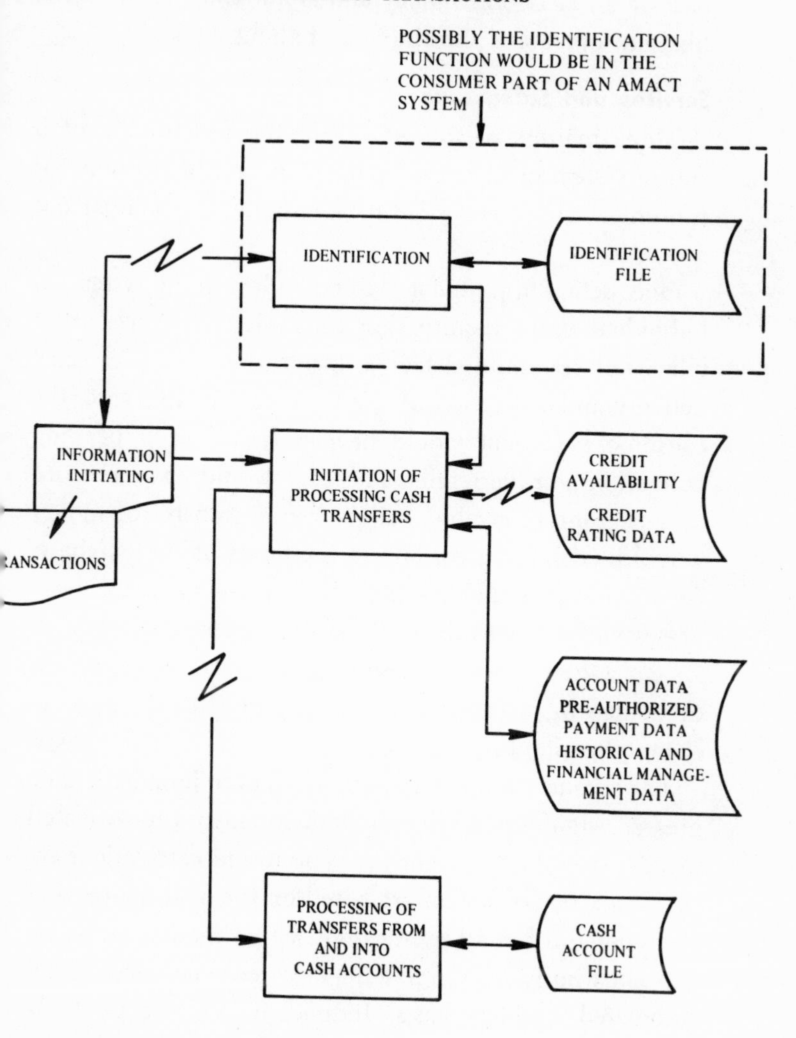
INTER-BUSINESS TRANSACTIONS
POSSIBLY THE IDENTIFICATION FUNCTION WOULD BE IN THE CONSUMER PART OF AN AMACT SYSTEM
IDENTIFICATION
IDENTIFICATION FILE
INFORMATION INITIATING
INITIATION OF PROCESSING CASH TRANSFERS
CREDIT AVAILABILITY
CREDIT RATING DATA
ANSACTIONS
ACCOUNT DATA
PRE-AUTHORIZED PAYMENT DATA
HISTORICAL AND FINANCIAL MANAGE-MENT DATA
PROCESSING OF TRANSFERS FROM AND INTO CASH ACCOUNTS
CASH ACCOUNT FILE
TELEPHONE COMMUNICATION

accounts in banks will be debited and credited on a regular and predictable basis. (The way in which the interbusiness part of an electronic money and credit transfer system is likely to operate is illustrated in Exhibit 11.)

Services and Safeguards

Three matters of importance in the functioning of a future system of electronic money and credit transfer for consumers and among businesses should be pointed out specifically.

One, delays in payment, will be built into the system, as individual cases require. For example, the buyer of a television set could delay payment to the retailer until delivery and inspection of the purchase. In this case, the consumer's account would have a record of a pending obligation and the retailer's account would have a record of a pending receivable, but the actual transfer of money would be delayed according to the terms of the purchase. In other words, neither individual consumers nor businesses will fall into the clutches of a relentless, inhuman system automatically disposing of their money regardless of human or machine error and the individual's right to change his mind up to a point.

The second matter of importance is even broader and of greater significance to an individualistically oriented society. It is this: Current projections and calculations regarding a future system are based on the assumption that up to one-third of all transactions within the United States will not wholly or even to a major extent take place on an automated, cashless basis. Individual preferences, legal requirements, and cost factors will always preserve the use of checks, currency, and even barter as acceptable means of exchange. Undoubtedly, the use of these means will continue to shrink in both relative and absolute terms as the electronic system becomes more flexible and more sophisticated. But, just as today we have forms of barter in hard goods (automobile trade-ins, for example) and in corporate acquisitions, the future will also leave room for older forms of transactions.

Finally, there is the matter of privacy. Fear has been expressed that the availability of individuals' total financial records, concentrated in one or two computer memories, will present dangerous opportunities for the invasion of fundamental rights. Actually there are at least two safeguards against this danger.

In the first place, the operators of an automated system are likely to be entities in competition with each other. This competitive element is discussed more fully later. At this point, it can be stated that the competitive nature of the electronic money and credit transfer business should offer substantial protection against the exploitation of private information by the businesses operating the system. It is probable, however, that strict legislation will be needed to prevent governmental interference at all levels, similar to the current wire-tapping problem.

In the second place, the very technology of the system should offer protection against random or criminal misuse of private information. The various pieces of information on individuals will be stored in a manner that will make it available only in the form of answers to a very specific and limited set of questions. The retrieval of other types of information will involve basic searches through the electronic files at relatively high costs. Legislation probably should be enacted to make such searches allowable only at the discretion of the individual to whom this information pertains. Thus, the technology protects the individual against the misuse of specific bits of information more effectively than do the mainly uncoded and written documents in today's filing systems.

THE ECONOMIC DEMANDS FOR CHANGE

It is generally accepted that national economic activity must at least double over the next fifteen years in order to meet the expected demands of a growing population for greater quantities of higher-quality goods and services. According to detailed projections developed by my firm, the number of financial transactions and the volume of data exchanged and recorded in connection with them will have to increase two to five times over current levels—depending on the specific type of operation—in order to support the required expansion of economic activity. These projections are based on a correlation of past trends and the application of certain of these trends to some of the most promising business innovations in such areas as credit facilities, leasing arrangements, and checking-account operations. However, there is one fundamental difficulty with the projected increases: They cannot and will not take place, unless the very nature of the transactions and the data themselves are basically and radically changed.

The ultimate result of this difficulty, if it remains unresolved, would be felt in macroeconomic (national) terms. The current system of money-and-credit transfer could not support the needed expansion of national economic activity. To project a doubling of gross national product by 1983 on the basis of current means of financial transactions is similar to expecting the 1968 volume of telephone calls to be made through the 1948 telephone system, with its reliance on operators, limited local dialing, no long-distance dialing, mechanical switching, and so on. Purely physical problems, as well as the resulting dollar costs, would be prohibitive, both in the example of telephone calls and to the projected economic expansion.

But a competitive economic system, with the appropriate technologies available to it, need not be threatened seriously with such a bogging down of its vital processes. The technological aspect is dealt with further on. Here, certain aggregates of the microeconomic (business or industry) aspects of the volumes and costs of financial exchange are discussed.

Examples of the projected two-to-five-fold increases in the number of financial and data exchange transactions are:

- A more than twofold increase in the amount of longer term (more than 30 days) consumer credit outstanding, from $95 billion to $220 billion.
- A close to threefold increase in consumer credit repayment transactions, from 2.2 billion to 6 billion annually.
- A fivefold increase in the number of consumer credit operations—that is, individual applications for short, revolving, and longer-term credit, from 300 million to 1.5 billion annually.
- A two- to threefold increase in transactions now involving the writing, drawing, and depositing of checks by individual consumers and by business

enterprises, from 17 billion to 40 or 45 billion annually.

The current costs of performing these money-and-credit transactions, at 1968 levels, for banks, other financial institutions, and business enterprises are estimated by our researchers to total some $13 billion annually. No estimates are attempted on costs to consumers, in terms of time spent and losses. The $13 billion of costs to the financial and business communities include operating expenses, as well as losses resulting from fraud or error. About $6 billion derive directly from credit transactions, about $7 billion from check transfers. Looked at from another angle, about $7 billion of these costs are borne by banks and other financial institutions, $6 billion by the rest of the business community.

The current $13-billion annual costs of financial transactions would increase to some $35 billion annually, if the present system were to expand sufficiently to support a twofold increase in national economic activity. But, even if such costs could be borne, it is highly unlikely that they will be, if any alternative is available. And, as already indicated, it is quite probable that the purely physical mechanics of the financial system would break down before the volume of transactions associated with the $35-billion annual-cost projection could be reached.

Therefore, new means for handling these volumes of transactions are being developed and will, over the next ten to fifteen years, change fundamentally the way in which money-and-credit transfers are consummated, as well as the role of financial institutions in our society.

These changes will be based on the vastly improved information and communications technologies already available or emerging from the laboratories and on a fundamental re-evaluation of markets by banks and other business enterprises that will operate a future system of electronic money-and-credit transfer.

TECHNOLOGICAL CAPABILITIES AND COSTS

Most of the technologies needed for the operation of a fully automated money-and-credit transfer system in the United States are available today. And, importantly, they are available at prices that would offer substantial cost savings for projected 1982 volumes of transactions, even if total system effectiveness—that is, the part of total national financial transactions integrated into the system—were only one-third instead of the probable two-thirds.

The Technologies

Very broadly, the technologies needed in a future system can be placed into the following categories. (Their places and general roles within the system are also illustrated in Exhibits 10 and 11.)

Terminal Equipment

Terminals will consist of devices placed in banks, homes, and retail and service establishments to permit communication with the central processors and files. The terminals will be of the building-block type (modules) that may be assembled to meet the specific requirements of the home or business establishment in which they are located. They may include a touch-tone type of input, a card-reader, and an audio-response unit, as well as several lights indicating system conditions and replies.

Thus, the terminals would be little more than variations, with accessories, of the touch-tone telephones that are beginning to be installed by the Bell Telephone System and are expected to be in widespread use by the end of the 1970's. Credit-card and similar types of information could be entered via the pushbuttons or with a device similar to the automatic card-dialer already available from Bell. This relatively simple and inexpensive type of terminal system could be integrated with more complex information (data-utility) terminals in business establishments desiring to do so. At any rate, the terminal devices for electronic money-and-credit transfer will add relatively small amounts to the basic costs of future telephone and data-utility services for those using one or both of these services in the first place.

Communications

Communications may well be provided through a type of Wide Area Telephone Service (WATS). This is a service that permits a customer, by using an access line, to make calls within a specificed zone for a flat monthly charge. It is now being offered on an outward basis nationally and is experimentally available on an inward basis in several states.

Inward WATS appears most suitable for communications in an automated money-and-credit-transfer system. The communications element, as a whole, may account for up to 50 per cent of total system costs, depending, in part, on federal and state regulatory policy decisions and, in part, on expected improvements in the existing technologies and operating procedures used by U.S. common carriers.

Central Processing Units and Mass Storage Files

The computing power of currently available third-generation central processors and the capacities of currently available random-access or disc-type memories are fully adequate to the demands of a future system. For example, the Burroughs 5500, RCA Spectra 70/55, IBM System 360/50, or CDC 3600 computers, ranging in average cost from $1.1 million to $2.3 million each, could serve consumer transactions in any specific region or metropolitan area. Also, on a regional basis, computers such as the Digital Equipment Corporation's PDP-6, the CDC 3300, and the Scientific Data Systems Sigma 7, ranging in average cost from $600,000 to $800,000 each, could serve interbusiness transactions.

Programming and Systems-Analysis Design and Installation

These techniques, as developed today, are perfectly adequate to the needs of an automated money-and-credit transfer system. However, they are costly and subject to great variations depending on the skills of the personnel involved and the diversity and sophistication of the system required. This last element—the variables of system complexity—could well be attributed, at least partly, to marketing costs. The specific services provided, including various safety factors and amounts of information made available to users, will depend to a large extent on user demands, as well as on regulatory and insurance requirements.

Voice Recognition

The one technology that is not available in commercially marketable form at this time is represented by voice-recognition units. These probably are fundamental to the security of procedures that electronically debit and credit cash accounts, as well as to the privacy and safety of individuals desiring to make medium-sized and larger purchases on credit. It is expected that voice recognition units will be commercially available by the mid-1970's. They will consist of devices that generate voice spectrograms as the result of voice inputs. These spectrograms will then be converted to digital formats for comparison with the digitalized voice patterns in the identification files of individuals. The technology and the communications time needed for this type of identification procedure are projected to account for a substantial part of the total system operating costs.

The Costs

Most of the hardware costs of a future system will be reduced by more than one-half during the next ten to fifteen years. Programming and related costs will also be relatively reduced but not by as much. Marketing and managerial costs are very difficult to estimate but can be safely assumed, on the basis of past experience, to equal hardware and software costs, at least over the first few years, if capital investment expenditures are prorated over the same period.

All in all, it is projected that a national system of electronic credit-and-money transfer will cost about $4 billion annually to operate over the first five years of widespread, although not necessarily intensive, implementation. Basically it has little effect on operating costs whether one-third or two-thirds of all transactions, regionally or nationally, are made through the system. In either event, the equipment and other facilities will have to be there and will have to be paid for. Thus, the intensity of actual implementation is of relatively little interest to a discussion of technological and related cost factors, although, of course, it is vital to profitability.

THE MEANING FOR BANKING AND BUSINESS

On the basis of the projected volumes of financial and data transactions and the technological costs of an automated system, rough estimates of cost savings and other business opportunities can be drawn.

Savings and Profits

The theoretical costs of credit-and-money transfer in the United States would be some $35 billion annually by 1983, if current ways of doing things continue unchanged. It is likely that up to one-third of total U.S. transactions around 1983 indeed will take place in a manner similar to today, while some two-thirds will be automated in a system along lines described above. Thus, the total costs of domestic financial transactions can be projected at some $16 billion annually by that time: $12 billion, more or less, for transactions that continue to be consummated outside an automated system plus $4 billion for the technological, marketing, and related costs of the new electronic system that will handle two-thirds of all transactions.

The figure of $16 billion annually represents a reasonable increase of less than 25 per cent in the total costs of handling transactions that will have increased two-to-five-fold in volume. The business opportunities for the operators and users of a future system and the benefits to the consuming public reside, in part, in the difference between the theoretical $35 billion cost of doing things as they are being done now and the projected $16-billion cost of doing them through the application of advanced computer and communications technologies. In part, also, these opportunities and benefits reside in the totally new services and conveniences that an automated system will provide. And, more broadly, the interest in such a system, both for operators and users, resides in the probability that the purely physical problem of handling the increased volumes of transactions by current means would prevent a substantial part of these transactions from being made at all. In other words, an automated system not only will provide cost savings and new opportunities but will make possible the volume of transactions from which these benefits derive.

It is not easy to make specific predictions on the extent to which various enterprises will actually operate parts or all of a future system. Therefore, the attribution of savings, profits, and other benefits also is difficult to project at this time. Much depends on the planning abilities and the negotiating strengths of the various interests involved, both regionally and nationally. However, it is possible to identify the types of enterprises that will be involved in the competitive struggle for the markets provided by a future system, and to do so in the context of the problems facing them.

Marketing

Since our economy is consumer oriented, a large measure of the problems facing most of the potential operators of an automated system is in marketing. The consumers and other potential systems-users must be sold on the conveniences, financial benefits, and increased safety and personal privacy that such a system offers.

For example, customers, including both the consuming public and business enterprises using the system, will have available to them, at the push of telephone touch-tone knobs, a complete picture of their latest financial position: obligations, assets, predicted income, and outgo. They will have this without having to balance check books, calculate real interest rates, or project predictable future expenditures.

Also, for a fee, financial services provided through the system will advise customers regarding their optimal payment and investment schedules, obviating the need for individuals to juggle payments against income in often inefficient attempts to make the most of their float. Finally, accounts and records kept in computer memories will protect customers against accidental and, in most cases, against premeditated disclosure of their financial positions to unauthorized eyes.

These, then, are some of the things that the operators of an automated system have to sell. The marketing of these and other benefits is one of their major challenges. The way they meet this challenge will determine to a large extent both how the technologies available are applied and who will own and operate these applications.

Potential Systems Operators, Owners, and Users

In this context, one can identify the groups that will be involved and, to a limited degree, the nature of their involvement.

Commercial Banks

In spite of the generally disorganized initial response of the banking community, as noted at the beginning of this chapter, it is difficult to believe that commercial banks will not play a major part in both the ownership and the operation of an automated system. Any other possibility would imply their abdication of the central role in our nation's financial affairs that they have sought and played with increasing aggressiveness. The real questions are: How many mistakes will the banks make on the way and how much will those mistakes cost them, in terms of money and effective control of a future system?

Other Financial Institutions

Enterprises ranging from savings-and-loan banks and investment houses to credit-card companies also have an important role in our current system. However, in some cases it is a peripheral role, while in others, such as with the more important credit-card companies, it reaches into the very heart of the consumer and retailer markets for an electronic system. American Express, for example, in 1969 reportedly increased its travel and entertainment card business by some 33 per cent over 1968. The future part of these institutions depends, much more than that of commercial banks, on the success of their immediate plans to obtain relatively invulnerable market positions, regionally or nationally. If they succeed in this, it will be difficult for others to edge or buy them out of significant ownership and operational roles. If they do not succeed, they will be absorbed by the future operators, or even cast aside.

Major Retailers

Although major retail establishments do have a considerable interest in consumer-credit operations, this is primarily considered as supportive of their merchandizing business. Some of the very biggest retail stores are still holding out against bank credit cards. But they may be forced into defense action because smaller retailers, who, until now were rarely in the position to offer credit, are signing up with the large bank and other credit-card plans. This represents potentially serious competition for major retailers, and it is quite possible that they will seek an ownership—and, in some cases, an operational—role in a future system, in order to protect the customer relationships that they help to maintain through their credit activities. It seems more likely, however, that, in most instances, major retailers will find it more profitable to safeguard their interests through their weight as users or customers of the services that future systems will offer. Nevertheless, this may well vary among regions or cities, depending on the capabilities of banks and others, as well as on managerial decisions among the retailers.

Computer and Other Manufacturers

There is a distinct possibility that such companies, especially those in the computer field, may wish to enter into the operations of money-and-credit transfer. This would involve some major diversification moves, which could be justified in terms of a defensive strategy or as extensions of internally effective computer-communications operations. The variables in this possibility are so great that it would be futile at this time to indicate more than just the potential interests and capabilities of such manufacturing companies.

Communications Companies

The very nature of a future system points to the importance of communications. However, whether communications companies will merely service or actually own and operate parts of such a system depends again on the effectiveness and plans of banks and others. Another important variable in this case concerns governmental regulatory decisions regarding common carriers.

The Changes in the Nature of Businesses

It should be clear from the foregoing discussion that the other major challenge, next to technological application and marketing, facing future operators and owners of an automated system resides in the potential obsolescence of the products and services they currently offer. In order to make up for the effect of this on sales and profits, they will have to evolve new markets. A number of examples come readily to mind.

Computer manufacturers probably will sell fewer machines to individual banks and businesses within a future system. They will have to sell hardware and services to the system itself. Major retailers may have to extend credit *through* the system instead of individually. Credit-card companies will find their services being absorbed by a future system unless they stake out their market segments by offering other services now. Commercial banks will see the *need for* and *profits from* demand deposits shrink, as automated money-and-credit transfers allow businesses and individuals to operate with relatively smaller liquid balances. They will have to seek sources of revenue from the operation of the system itself and through new services, such as the highly sophisticated management of individual and business accounts.

Thus, not only will the means of financial transactions change; the very nature of many businesses will also be substantially different. We will be in a time when money grows in computers, and those who wish to obtain their portion will have to learn new ways of reaping this harvest.

About 2,000 years ago a man called Publilius Syrus said that "money alone sets all the world in motion." This may be true. But what keeps the world going and determines its speed is the way money itself moves. When money moved slowly and erratically, the world moved slowly and by bits and starts. The future demands that the world move quickly and safely. And this means that some system must and will develop in which money (and credit) moves quickly and safely.

A probable future course of events toward this end in the United States is outlined in this chapter. In other parts of the world—Western Europe, for example—the timing and the substance of events are likely to be somewhat different. But this is in itself a subject for a detailed discussion, including an analysis of its relation and importance to the financial and business communities of the United States.

Of course, events take on quite unexpected shapes. And this, perhaps, would really be the least startling thing about the so-called cashless society. Nothing is easier or safer to predict than the unpredictability of events moved by men. And, although money may set the world in motion, men move money. Ultimately, the outcome rests on entrepreneurial and managerial decisions, which take into account the internal enterprise needs and the new market demands created by technological change: the old ways of operating and the old sources of revenue foreclosed, and the new opportunities opening up for banking and other industries.

Chapter 10

A BASIC LOOK AT ONE'S JOB: A CASE STUDY OF THE NEWSPAPER PUBLISHING INDUSTRY

The central core of the newspaper publishing business is changing. Here, perhaps more than in any other industry, we find that fundamental change in the business is profoundly affecting the relations of that business with the society it serves.

New editorial capabilities are made available to the editor by information and communications technologies. By 1978, the editorial office will be totally different from what it is today. Through the use of light pencils, the editor will be able to change copy displayed on screens mounted on his desk. He will be able to call for supplementary material from electronic morgues and news libraries. After consultation with other editors and reporters, who will have similar devices at their desks, the editor will be able instantly to print the copy as it appears on his screen. As a consequence of these and other developments, the editor will have vastly increased flexibility and will be able rapidly and continually to change the contents of the newspaper.

Flowing from these technologies will come other changes in what a newspaper does. For example, instant access to electronic files will put the publisher into the information business, serving individual and corporate subscribers. And, of course, the way of operating already is changing: in the business office, in advertising, in the press room, and in distribution.

Rather than allow other technologically based media to encroach further on the markets of the newspaper business, the industry can bring about a new era in journalism. As important as the new technology is to the editor and the publisher, only by considering the implications to the entire enterprise can the newspaper survive.

This chapter is based on an address before the annual meeting of the American Society of Newspaper Editors in Washington, D.C., April 19, 1963.

The newspaper industry represents a case study in which a new technology is changing the central core of the business—even though the initial perception of this has been limited primarily to procedural and cost-saving matters. The changes are especially profound for the editor, whose job is about to alter fundamentally, but it is profound too for the enterprise itself. Newspapers, like railroads and banks, are close to the demands of society. And perhaps this position of newspaper publishing is closer to the heart of societal concern than the other cases. Railroads and banks will, through their uses of technology, affect our economic standard of life. Newspapers, however, are integral to our freedoms. The interaction between business and social change is most evident here.

Automation in its most obvious sense—reduced costs through improved procedures—spells survival for many of America's newspapers. There are few industries where the economics of automation are so starkly etched, so portentous for the community, or so long overdue. But automation means more than the economics of survival. It means, too, major and inexorable change in nearly every aspect of newspaper publishing—mechanical change, business change, and most of all, *editorial* change. (Exhibits 12 to 16 illustrate the expected impact.)

To date, virtually everything that has been said about automation and newspapers has been related to change on the mechanical side, not on the editorial. Yet, automation is going to change totally the way in which a newspaper is edited—the environment in which editors work, the tools that they use, and the kind of editorial product that they produce.

EXHIBIT 12

NEWSPAPER—EDITOR'S DESK 1978

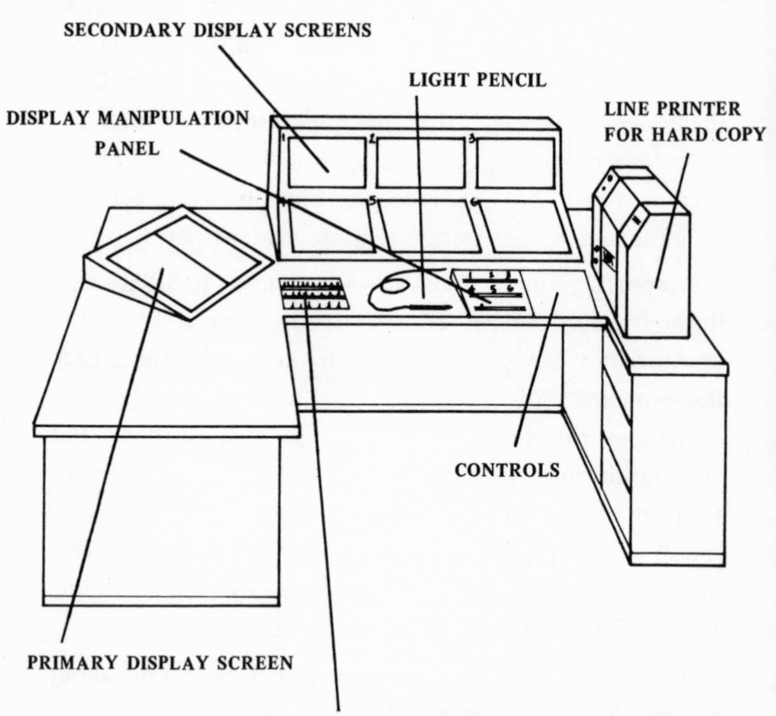

HIBIT 13

1968 NEWSPAPER OPERATION USING COMPUTER

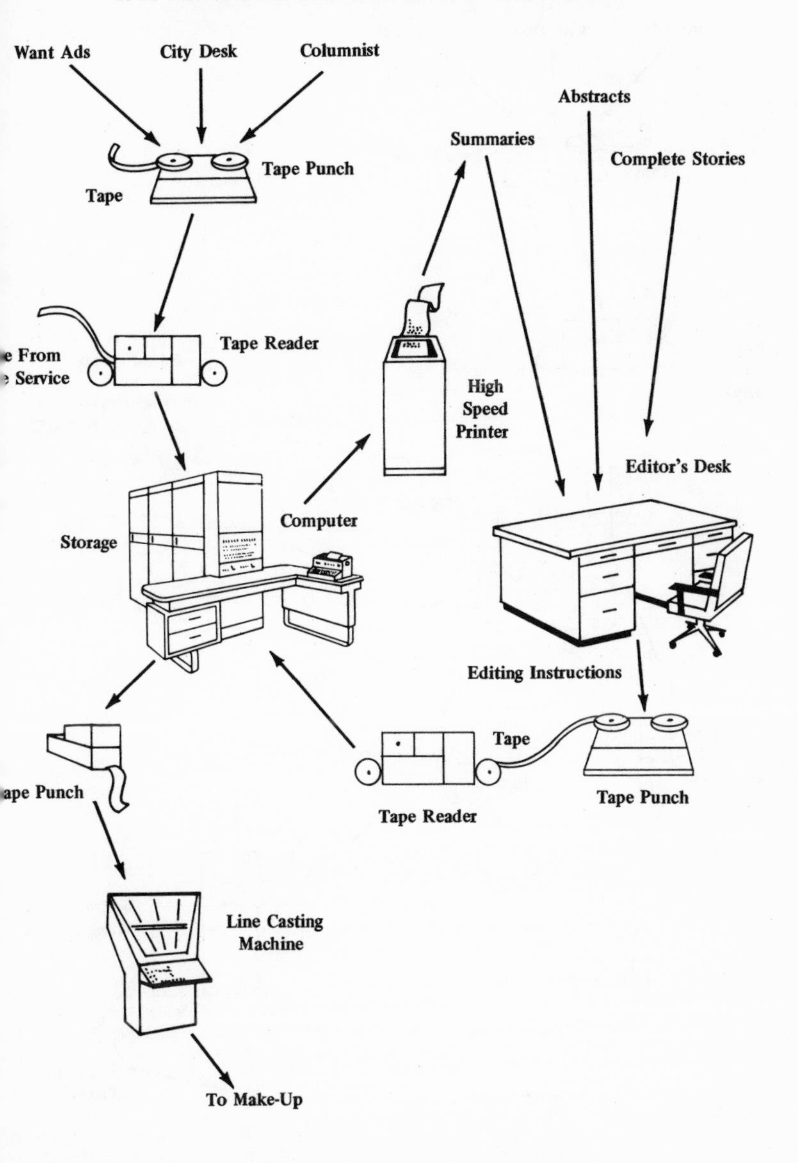

EXHIBIT 14

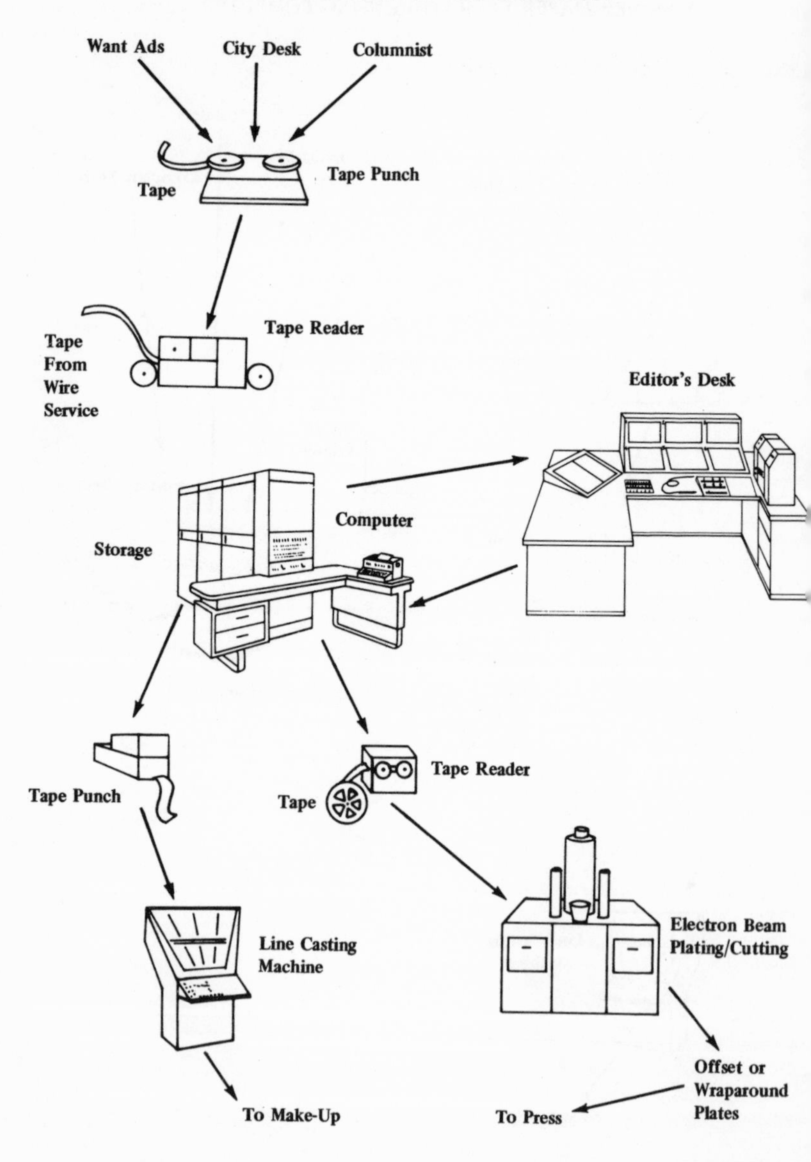
NEWSPAPER OF THE LATE 1970's
Want Ads
City Desk
Columnist
Tape
Tape Punch
Tape From Wire Service
Tape Reader
Editor's Desk
Storage
Computer
Tape Punch
Tape Reader
Tape
Line Casting Machine
Electron Beam Plating/Cutting
To Make-Up
Offset or Wraparound Plates
To Press

HIBIT 15

MPACT OF INFORMATION TECHNOLOGY ON NEWSPAPER OPERATIONS 1968-1978

INFORMATION TECHNOLOGY	AREAS OF NEWSPAPER OPERATIONS					
	Editorial	**Composing**	**Printing**	**Distribution**	**Advertising**	**Business**
Small to Medium EDP Systems	Some Impact	Some Impact	Little or No Impact	Little or No Impact	Some Impact	Great Impact
Large Scale Real Time EDP Systems	Great Impact	Some Impact	Some Impact	Some Impact	Great Impact	Some Impact
Information Storage And Retrieval System	Great Impact	Little or No Impact	Little or No Impact	Little or No Impact	Great Impact	Some Impact
High Speed Data Transmission	Great Impact	Little or No Impact	Little or No Impact	Little or No Impact	Little or No Impact	Little or No Impact
Satellite Operations Using Data Communications	Little or No Impact	Some Impact	Some Impact	Some Impact	Little or No Impact	Little or No Impact
Key Board Input Devices	Great Impact	Little or No Impact	Little or No Impact	Little or No Impact	Little or No Impact	Little or No Impact
Inexpensive Photo - Composition	Little or No Impact	Little or No Impact	Little or No Impact	Some Impact	Little or No Impact	Little or No Impact
Electronic Display System	Great Impact	Little or No Impact	Little or No Impact	Little or No Impact	Great Impact	Little or No Impact

Great Impact   **Some Impact**   **Little or No Impact**

EXHIBIT 16

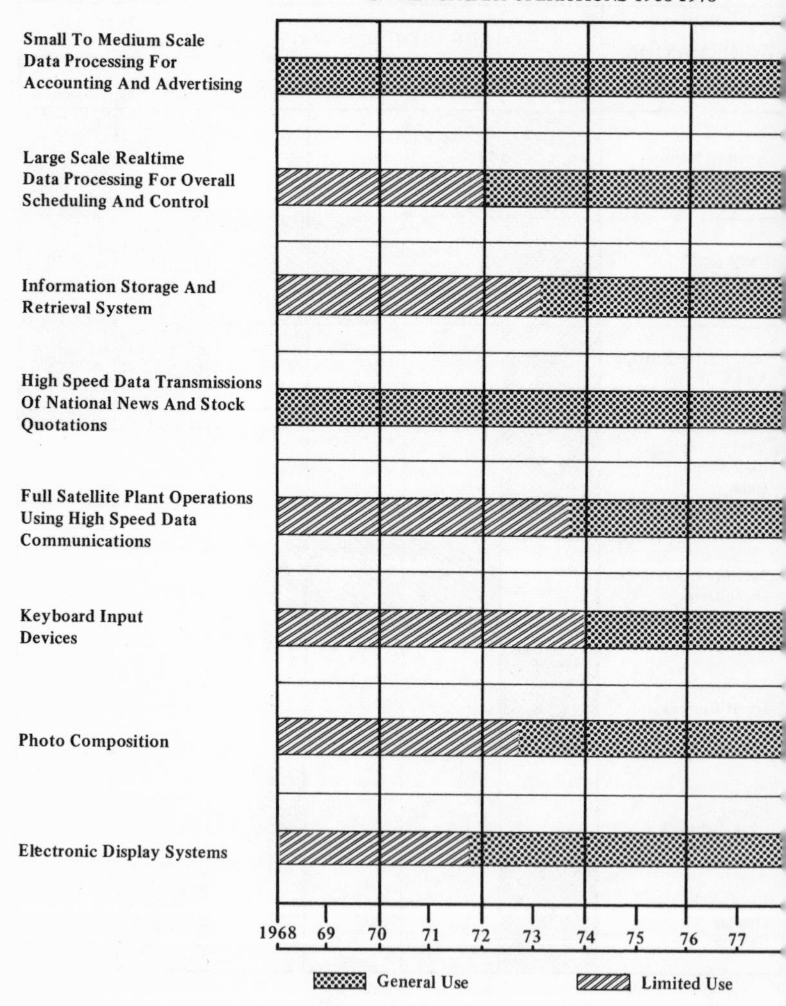
TIMING OF IMPACT OF INFORMATION TECHNOLOGY
ON NEWSPAPER OPERATIONS 1968-1978
Small To Medium Scale
Data Processing For
Accounting And Advertising
Large Scale Realtime
Data Processing For Overall
Scheduling And Control
Information Storage And
Retrieval System
High Speed Data Transmissions
Of National News And Stock
Quotations
Full Satellite Plant Operations
Using High Speed Data
Communications
Keyboard Input
Devices
Photo Composition
Electronic Display Systems
1968
69
70
71
72
73
74
75
76
77
General Use
Limited Use

THE IMPACT OF TECHNOLOGY

Three things are going to happen to newspaper work in the next ten years as a result of information and communications technologies.

Changes in the Tools of the Trade

The function of editor will remain the same, but the tools he uses to perform his function will change greatly.

For example, an editorial copy will be fed into a computer-like system upon arrival in the office—whether it comes in by wire, is typed in by a reporter, or is called up from the morgue. The copy will be manipulated electronically, displayed on TV screens that will be a part of every editorial desk, and dummied by manipulating the information on the screen with light pencils and light erasers.

There will be powerful new tools for editorial research. The morgue will be electronic, rapid, and selective. More editorial services will be available on a commercial basis from firms using electronic libraries and selling the service by wire, such as the UPI system announced in April, 1969.

In short, the editorial office of 1978 will be quite a different place from what it is today. It will be new; it will be fascinating; it will provide tools that will remove some of today's mechanical handicaps; and that will result in a better editorial product.

Changes in the Production System

The editor will be much closer to the reader in both time and space. Many newspapers will print simultaneously at a number of locations on light presses. The time from the editor's desk to the printed page will be reduced to a few minutes. Edition-to-edition changes will be easier than today and less costly.

There will be no more typesetting in most newspapers, for the page image approved on the display screen will be transmitted directly to the printing plate, when the editor touches a final approval button. Thus, editorial changes will be possible and economical up to the moment of going into print.

In short, to a far greater extent than today imaginable, it will be possible to respond rapidly to a changing situation. Instead of continuing to encroach upon editorial work, the mechanical side of the business can be made to respond more closely to the editor's needs.

New Forms of the Publishing Enterprise and New Editorial Services

Publishing firms will offer new kinds of services to other papers, as well as to the public. Electronic morgue services and special local and regional information will be sold by publishers over the data-transmission facilities of our telephone system. Supplementary and specialized publications will be increasingly compiled, using the extensive material on hand and easily accessible in an electronic editorial system. This will do for newspapers what book publishing is doing for magazines.

The New Idea

Except for banking, there is no industry that is going to be more completely changed in the next decade as the result of automation—nor one that today realizes it less. If many of these things sound farfetched, it should be emphasized that, as in electronic money-and-credit transfer, almost no new scientific breakthroughs are needed to allow any of these changes to take place. All that is needed is the engineering of existing science to fit the needs of newspapers. What is new is the *idea* of engineering information technology to the needs of the editor.

THE EDITORIAL OFFICE

The remainder of this chapter is primarily concerned wtih a description of the editorial office of 1978 and the new tools that will be available. Briefly stated, production and publishing changes will mean that, whatever the editor is doing now, he will be able to do better with the 1978 system, because he will have better control over the production of the newspaper. The technological changes in other portions of the newspaper will be fully as extensive as will the editorial office changes. Properly applied, they will help to produce a system far more responsive to the editorial needs than is true today.

The editorial office of 1978 will differ greatly from the one of today. At its heart will be an electronic information system connecting editorial desks, wire services, morgue, an electronic news library, and the composing room. All of the editorial copy that comes into the paper by the wire service, by telephone, or in the office typewriters will be introduced directly into this system. The UPI system mentioned above, for example, is expected to deliver, within a few years, copy at 1,050 words a minute—on a computer-to-computer basis—at the time desired and in a format geared to the individual client's production needs. The system will store copy in a number of ways, just as an electronic computer today stores information introduced into it.

Just as today's electronic computer handles words and sentences as well as numbers, and is able to manipulate these words, even translating them into another language, so the 1978 newspaper system will handle editorial copy, storing it in memory, transmitting it from one area to another, and printing it out by automatic typewriter or high-speed printer.

But, unlike most of today's computers, the 1978 editorial system will have not one but many control points for communicating with the system. Just as the system will accept information from many sources, so it will respond at many points to questions placed to the system for display of the information contained in the system. In this manner, many editors' and reporters' desks will be connected to the system, allowing them the opportunity to introduce new information, look at and alter what is already in the system, and rearrange copy and photos (which will be stored in rather the same manner as the text).

Tools and Techniques

Editorial direction of the system will be exercised through editing consoles, which will provide the following tools and techniques for editorial work.

Display screens. Similar in appearance to TV sets, display screens will be mounted on editors' desks. Using the screens, editors will be able to obtain a projection of a full page or combination of pages of the edition on which they are working or of any earlier edition. They will be able to project images of any copy that has been, or is being, introduced into the central computer system by reporters, editors, or the wire services, and ascertain immediately the size, position, and changes in the "news hole." Thus, they will be able to determine, at a glance, the consequences on other stories and pages of shifts in layout or copy.

The image editors see on the display screen will be the type of the individual paper. However, it will exist only in the electronic trace on the screen. It will not be the image that has been set and it will not be transferred to a printing plate until a few minutes before it is ready to print.

It will therefore be possible to alter it at will, increasing or decreasing the size of photos or headlines, adding to a story from extra copy (displayed on one of the auxiliary screens) that was not used originally, or cutting as other news breaks occur.

Light pencils. Similar to small flashlights, light pencils will enable the editors to draw circles around portions of the display they wish to delete and see it vanish, though they will be able to recall it later if they wish to do so. They will be able to erase anything they wish, and move photos and enlarge, reduce, eliminate, or crop them. They will be able to point out items to be expanded, reduced, or eliminated and immediately see the results of such changes.

In other words, the editors and their staffs will be able to dummy continuously, immediately, and without extra cost. This will permit them to see the consequences of various changes and freeze in metal the form of presentation chosen at the last possible moment before printing.

Secondary display screens. Around the editors' desks, secondary screens will allow them to work efficiently with a number of alternative sources of editorial copy. They will be able to review material that spills over onto other pages, study original copy and unused portions of a story, and display background material from the morgue.

Input keyboards. Similar to a typewriter on the desk, keyboards will let editors alter any display by pushing one of a number of buttons connected to the central system. Using the typewriter keyboards, they will be able to specify the material to be displayed on the screen and specify column width, page layout, type font, and size. Thus, they will be able to type in any additions of their own or any additions they may choose to use from material displayed on secondary screens.

Magnetic-tape files. Part of the central information system, magnetic tape files will hold all the copy for a single edition or series of editions. By using the display screens and keyboard, editors will be able to print out, from an office-copier-type of device at the desk, "hard copy" of any material in the system and review the makeup on any page, by calling it up for display on any of the editing screens.

News libraries. The central repositories for picture sources and all the raw copy fed into the computer by the wire services, the reporters, and the editors will be news libraries. These will store some copy by magnetic means, but much will be stored optically in such a manner that it can be retrieved immediately for display or print-out at the editors' desks, enabling them to refer instantly to any additional material needed, such as a comparison of various wire-service reports on the same story, and to browse through the copy available on any story at any time by letting it pass over the TV screen or by printing it out on paper.

Electronic morgues. One of the most important parts of the editorial intelligence system will be, in effect, electronic libraries that will replace today's morgues. The electronic morgues will store information by electromechanical and optical means. Editors will be able to obtain displays of actual documents, clippings, and stories that have been stored and indexed by the computer; obtain prints from earlier editions, which have been stored photographically; and indicate the category or kind of information that is needed and let the computer select it.

Aided by such electronic morgues, editors will be able to obtain more relevant background for a news break that occurs only minutes before press time. The computer can be instructed to select from those portions of morgue material only what relates directly to the story, display them on a screen, or print them out in the form of hard copy at the desk.

The Editor's Job

Using the 1978 editorial system, each editor and reporter will continue to work independently, but communication among them and with the system itself will be vastly improved. Editors will be able to talk with each other about the content of various pages, exchange views about specific stories and the best use of available material, and conduct a running argument about how the paper should be put together, all the while sitting at ease at their desks, each looking at the consequences of alternative suggestions without pouring any hot metal.

Inherent in the system will be the editor's ability to retrieve almost instantaneously whatever information or material he may need in order to make decisions on layout and make-up. By pushing the proper buttons on his keyboard, he will be able to retrieve material from the computer's tape file, news library, or morgue and project it on his display screens. He will be able to control the entire format of the paper and alter it in a matter of minutes.

When the editor is satisfied with a page or section, he can press a "print button" and transmit an exact image of the page to one or several locations, where the printing plates will be prepared automatically by, in effect, exposing them to the same electronic traces he sees on his screens, but using considerably higher energy levels so that, instead of merely leaving a trace, metal is actually removed by the electron beam—as is now done in some aerospace electron-beam machining. An alternative may well be a very much faster form of photocomposition, with similar electronic actuation.

Unlike today, transmission will be at very high rates of speed—a full page in an instant. (We are today successfully, though experimentally, transmitting data at the rate of 20 million bits per second, the equivalent of a volume of the *World Book Encyclopedia* every three minutes.) The plate cutting will be done equally fast, in about two minutes per plate.

Eventually, printing will be electrostatic with no plates at all, allowing continuous variations—single copy-to-copy changes—in newspaper editions. Some of the transmission may well be to the recording device that will be a part of home TV sets. But that is probably getting beyond 1978, although this has been done experimentally in Japan over the past few years.

The State of Technological Change

The roots or technical essence of every one of these developments exists today. Newspaper science writers are familiar with most of them—military command-control networks with wall-sized displays that change as military conditions alter; the now obsolete SAGE system, using light pencils and erasers; the Air Force aerial photographs, called up rapidly and automatically from the morgues; or the information retrieval systems of the intelligence services. All these are precursors of tomorrow's editorial office.

This is not the place to describe the technology that makes possible such systems. This is done in preceding chapters. It is useful to mention, however, why it is we can create such systems today.

Technological change will be extensive, partly because the technology important to newspapers no longer depends upon sporadic developments and isolated mechanical inventions. We now have a solid base in theory for attacking the problem of newspaper automation right across the board.

Since the newspaper business is the business of handling and communicating information, the fundamental changes taking place in information and communications technologies are going to alter greatly every aspect of newspaper work. Information-systems technology—the same technology that allows us to build TELSTAR, translating machines, computers that can abstract documents, and machines that respond to the spoken voice—provides the basis for an overhaul and fundamentally change the entire system of newspaper publication.

Applied to other aspects of newspaper publishing, this

same technology is going to change substantially the business office, the advertising process, the press room, and the distribution of the paper itself. The seeds of change, in media-selection by computer models, in press-scheduling, in truck-routing by computer, can be seen all about us, within the industry and in the related problems of other industries.

Among others, the *Los Angeles Times,* the *Oklahoman,* the *Palm Beach Post Times,* and the *South Bend Tribune* have all installed electronic computers through which editorial copy is run. The computer justifies lines, hyphenates words, and punches paper tape for running the linotype machines. The *Wall Street Journal* and *The New York Times* are using teletype setting and, in the case of the *Journal,* facsimile for multilocation printing, pioneering tomorrow's high-speed multiplant printing.

Overseas, the Japanese newspaper *Asahi Shimbun* prints several regional editions in different parts of the country through facsimile transmission and offset printing in the outlying plants and hot metal in the central office, a combination that may well foreshadow intermediate stages of future U.S. development. And in France, the major distributor of newspapers and magazines, NMPP (Nouvelles Messageries de la Presse Parisienne) achieves a degree of control otherwise unknown over a gigantic distribution system by most impressive use of a complex of electronic computers.

THE PROBLEMS OF TECHNOLOGICAL APPLICATION

Change of the magnitude described here is obviously going to produce great problems. Engineering the technology to specific requirements, while important and at times vexing, will probably be least among the problems to be faced. There are several more fundamental problems.

Editorial Initiative and Control

It is the editor who must decide what he wants to do with the technology of automation. It is the editor's imagination that should control the ends to which technology is to be applied. Automation is, in a sense, too important to leave to the publisher.

It is up to the editor to keep publishers, as well as the general public, informed as to what is going on in the world. If the decisions as to what to do with the technology of automation are left to the business side of the paper, it would mean abandoning one of the greatest editorial opportunities in the history of journalism.

Creatively used by the editor, this new tool of information technology can vastly improve the editorial reach, the quality or product, and the role of the newspaper in our society. Automation should be viewed as far more than a defensive weapon in the economics of publishing. Imaginatively used, it can allow newspapers to do a better job.

It is in coping with the problem of editorial awareness and leadership in the development of the newspaper information system that several needs emerge. The editorial profession, as a whole, might be well advised to seek, in an organized way, the means to identify developments in information and communications technologies of importance to newspaper editors. This would involve familiarizing its members with what it is that this new technology makes possible and providing a mechanism whereby editorial imagination is exercised in determining just what it is that editors, as a profession, want to do with the technology.

Without editorial guidance, one can expect piecemeal developments, representing solutions to other people's problems, to drift into use in the editor's office. It is far better to extend the range of editorial capability through conscious and imaginative planning than to adapt to solutions that come along looking for newspaper problems.

Social Innovations to Deal with the Human Problems of Transition

If labor problems arise as a result of minimal technological innovation, think of the problem of truly coping with the technology of the next decade. Social innovations must keep pace with the technological ones.

Anyone who thinks of the New York newspaper strikes in the 1960's as "automation strikes" should recognize that the mechanical improvements in New York represent more nearly a catching up with the state of technology of fifteen years ago than of facing the potential of today's technology. This perhaps serves to point up the human problem of future change, for the only thing that is really certain about the new technology is change—fundamental change.

Complete freedom of technological innovation is absolutely essential if newspapers are to take full advantage of this new technology. Technological change is going to mean a breakdown and regrouping in new ways of many traditional job and departmental lines. A new understanding with the unions is clearly necessary in order to forge the kind of newspaper system that is both feasible and desirable—desirable both in terms of survival for the industry and in terms of improved quality of service to the public.

A Clearly Defined Program

One of the most costly lessons we have learned thus far in applying the new technologies to other industries is the need for a clearly thought-out plan and program. This is discussed more fully in the preceding chapters but should be referred to in this context.

The whole concept of the new technologies derives from systems analysis, from the study of an organization process as a dynamic, ever changing, and completely interdependent system. The technological changes, as well as the organizational and human changes, must be handled not on a piecemeal basis but in terms of a clearly defined *system*.

None of this is to say that the changes must all occur overnight. It is far preferable to go at it step by step. There is an old proverb that the longest journey begins with a single step, and so it is with automation. But the steps should be according to a map that is drawn and agreed upon before the journey is started. Modest beginnings, which provide training for personnel and allow the organization an introduction to the technology, are highly desirable.

Equally important in applying information technology is an imaginative and fresh look at the basic problem. A good rule of thumb is, "Don't mechanize what you do today." Look, rather, at the real needs underlying today's procedures and try to apply technology to solving the basic problems rather than to mechanizing today's tasks.

Major technological change is going to shake to its foundations the entire newspaper industry in the next decade. There is little doubt about that but, also, it is clear that there are sharp and mixed reactions to this process. Editors, like bankers and machine tool men in their industries, more often than not are uneasy when they think about newspaper automation. Automation is viewed as encroaching on the editorial process. It is looked upon as mechanical and as originating in the efficiency departments of the business office, the very antithesis of all that is desirable in journalism, in finance, or in the running of any enterprise associated with great traditions of responsible service.

But technology was not always viewed in this manner by the editor. In an earlier day of our newspaper history, each new technology was grasped eagerly by the editors and aggressively applied. Telegraph, linotype, the high-speed press—these were the very foundations of modern journalism. It was in 1879 that Whitelaw Reid said:

> The business of making a newspaper is in a state of constant growth and change. You might almost say that it is revolutionized once every ten years. The veteran returns to find the old methods useless, the old weapons out of date, the old plans of action out of relation to the present arrangement of the forces. . . . The history of journalism, for fifty years, has been a rapid succession of revolutions, and no man knows as well as the hard-working editor that perfection has not yet been evolved.

One must look to tomorrow's technological change with the same attitude. It is only the editors who can apply technology creatively. It is incumbent upon them to familiarize themselves with what it can do and then to allow creativity and imagination, two pronounced characteristics of their profession, to lead them to totally new ways of using technology.

The new technologies becoming available, when used imaginatively, can lead to a far better editorial product. They can provide a more effective and imaginative attack on the problems of providing the public with news and information.

Two major technological revolutions of our time, radio and television, have had a sharp impact on newspapers. Yet the newspaper strikes in New York had the result of showing us once again the great role that can be filled only by newspapers. Indeed, the old could not be patched together indiscriminately, but the best of the old survived, and the beginnings of something new are emerging.

Newspapers have a place in society that can be made even more important by aggressive and far-sighted use of the new tools available. Rather than fighting a rear-guard action as every new technology allows other media to encroach further upon the newspaper business, technology can be used to open a new era in journalism. Imaginatively used by the editor and economically used by the publisher, the new technologies can make possible a new age of newspapers in this country and throughout the world.

Chapter 11

COMPUTERS, PROGRAM MANAGEMENT, AND FOREIGN AFFAIRS: A CASE STUDY OF FOREIGN AFFAIRS

There are important parallels between business and governmental experiences in the application of information and related technologies. Perhaps the most fundamental similarity resides in the need for a man at the top to understand the systems approach and to ensure its success. There are other similarities of interest to business management. But, since use of the new technologies will also change the substance of the conduct of foreign relations—as it is changing the substance of what business does—there are even more important elements for business planning in this case study. It is quite possible, for example, that the entire basis for trade negotiations will be altered by the use of information technology, including simulation and gaming techniques. The nature of treaties will change as the result of information in globally available data banks. Thus, investment policies and the allocation and use of international resources will be based on different criteria.

Just as in business, and probably much more so, fundamental human and political problems will prevent the use of technology from becoming a panacea in foreign-affairs management. In order to minimize these obstacles, training and organizational planning are required. The central question remains: What do we want from our technology? If we know, we can get it, in government as in business.

This chapter is based on an article originally published in the January, 1968, issue of Foreign Affairs.

The application of system techniques to foreign affairs is of interest to business for two major reasons. First, there are important similarities between the problems encountered by administrators in business and government—although one must be careful also to recognize the distinctions. Second, as the substance of the conduct of foreign affairs changes, business operations on the international scene will be profoundly affected.

Therefore, in this case study, an attempt is made to draw meaningful parallels between business and governmental experiences in applying the new technologies. Also, some indications are given of substantive areas of international relations—for example, trade negotiations and resource allocations—that may be changed by the application of the new technologies.

THE FRAMEWORK FOR TECHNOLOGICAL APPLICATIONS

Two directives issued by President Johnson began to provide the framework for testing the application of the newest tools of information and communications technologies to the conduct of foreign affairs. Since then, there has been much evidence, especially in testimony before and reports by the Senate Subcommittee on National Security and International Operations (chaired by Senator Henry M. Jackson), that both the organizational and human problems that must be solved in the State Department are substantial. However, it also seems quite clear that, if the new tools are effectively applied and gain wider acceptance, they could radically affect the management and even the substance of international relations.

On October 12, 1965, Johnson "directed the introduction of an integrated programming-planning-budgeting system (PPBS) in the executive branch," including the State Department. The system is a management method for measuring the effectiveness of expenditures in reaching program goals and appeared to have marked success when introduced by Secretary McNamara in the Defense Department. In implementing this system within the Defense Department there has been wide use of computer technology. Similar systems and technology are now being proposed and tested for the needs of the State Department.

The second directive was issued on March 4, 1966, when Johnson "directed the Secretary of State . . . to assume authority and responsibility for the over-all direction, coordination, and supervision of interdepartmental activities of the United States Government overseas." Within certain limitations, the Secretary thus received a charter to become the manager of our foreign affairs rather than merely the coordinator.

In 1969, Undersecretary of State Elliot L. Richardson, representing the Nixon Administration, issued a number of orders, based partly on the experience gained during the three preceding years, which envisaged major changes of the organizational framework within which foreign-affairs management would be carried out. But the thrust and purposes of the original directives remain unchanged.

Requisites for Success

Some of the details and historical aspects of the original plans and subsequent revisions are discussed later in this chapter. At this point it can be said, however, that the success with which the Secretary manages the State Department will depend to a great extent on his ability to meet its requirements for information and communications. These are now so complex that the question is no longer whether technology should be applied to meet them but how. The success of such technology within the Department depends critically on four factors: (1) sound analysis at the highest level of the information needs of the Department, (2) the effective application of information and communications technology to these needs, rather than simply the mechanization of the current inadequate information systems, (3) the communication of the information thus collected to those who need and must act upon it, and (4), most importantly, a man at the top—that is, in *senior management*—who wants the systems approach to succeed and who understands it. These requirements, of course, closely parallel those in business. There are lessons to be drawn on both sides—in the private sector and in government.

To those who conduct our foreign affairs, as to the manager of a private enterprise, information and communications technologies pose not only questions of application but also challenges of change. For, as we have seen in the preceding chapters, the application of technology not only changes the method by which an operation is performed, but frequently changes what is performed. Just as businesses are now able through technology to provide entirely new services to ever increasing numbers of people, so will the scope, conduct, and substance of foreign affairs change as technology is applied.

But, it must be emphasized that what is foreseen represents no panacea, no automated foreign service. As Harvard University Professor Thomas C. Schelling concluded, after the first eighteen months of State Department testing of PPBS:

> Foreign affairs is complicated and disorderly; its conduct depends mainly on the quality of the people who have responsibility; decisions have to be based on judgments, often too suddenly to permit orderly analytical processes to determine those decisions. The best—the very best—performance that is humanly possible is likely to look pretty unsatisfactory to the Congress, to Washington correspondents, to the electorate, even to the President who presides over the arrangement. The system can be improved, but not to anybody's complete satisfaction. In this improvement, PPBS will eventually have a significant role.

The purpose of this chapter is to underline the fact that the application of information and communications technologies to the improvement of the system raises major questions and requires the most thoughtful planning.

Some Substantive Effects

In all areas, not only in PPBS or even foreign affairs as such, the choices of instruments for decision and action are widening. The old obstacles to judgment and service are receding and are in the process of taking on new and, at this time, unpredictable shapes. It is my judgment, however, that as the new technology is applied to foreign affairs, reliance on personal judgment and personal and national moral standards will increase, not decrease. As the horizons of factual ignorance and misinformation fade, the decision-maker will be presented with vast new areas of choice.

If, for example, information systems are perfected by technology, what will be the role of the ambassador? He could have available instantly all the information and analysis available to the Secretary of State but might still lack the latter's over-all view of national priorities and interests. Two or three hundred years ago, when it required days, weeks, months, or, in same cases, years for an ambassador to reach his assignment or to communicate with his sovereign, he was indeed plenipotentiary. There was no choice. He knew more than anyone at home about conditions in his assigned country, and orders regarding the most fundamental and long-term actions could not, in most cases, reach him in time to be relevant. Over the past hundred years, with the coming of the telegraph, the wireless, the express train, and the jet, the role of the ambassador has diminished, at least in terms of his power to act. At home, the number of people who know as much about his mission as he does has increased. As a matter of fact, the ambassador's home office has at its disposal sources of information and analytical talents to which he has no access.

Now, however, the situation is changing again. If we so decide, the ambassador will be able to have all the information relevant to his assignment. He could once more be in fact plenipotentiary, if this were the wish of his superiors. On the other hand, as his home office will be able to be in even closer touch with his mission than before, the need to rely on the judgment of the man on the spot could diminish even further. When the leaders of nations can confer for hours, face to face, on closed-circuit television, will the ambassador's role become even more limited to that of an information-gatherer, pulse-taker and "holder-of-hands"? It is interesting to speculate on the kind of summitry we will have when such technologies really become effective.

Thus, the areas of choice between effective courses of action widen. Who makes the decisions? Who is the instrument of response? Other examples, perhaps more portentous in nature, will appear later. But even in the case of the ambassador, the implications for foreign-affairs management are not to be dismissed lightly. If some sort of middle course is chosen, let us say by making the power of the ambassador dependent on the sensitivity of his post or on his personal abilities, serious consequences to the prestige of our envoys could result. The fact that this problem has been developing for some time does not diminish its implications for the future. For, as the distance between alternative policies lengthens, deliberate or unconscious inconsistencies become both more obvious and more fraught with consequence.

THE NEED FOR CHANGE

Sir Winston Churchill, in discussing the process of making strategic wartime decisions, wrote: "Success depends on sound deductions from a mass of intelligence, often specialized and highly technical, on every aspect of the enemy's national life, and much of this information has to be gathered in peace-time." How much simpler the decision-making process might have been for him had it been possible then, as it is becoming increasingly so now, to centralize such information technologically.

The Proliferation of Information

Recent data gathered in connection with the testing of PPBS show that, in the State Department in Washington, some 2,000 telegrams are processed every day, and an average of 70 copies is made of each. The resultant 140,000 pieces of paper daily are filed both centrally and in various user files. The Central Foreign Policy file alone grows at the rate of 600 cubic feet (400 file drawers) a year. The Intelligence staff has 200 professional employees who read and try to analyze some 100,000 documents monthly. Most of this information is filed to meet the personal requirements of those in charge of various bureaus and offices. Its existence is not known or useful to others. Senior officers must wade through stacks of telegrams and airgrams to get a few bits of significant information. The new or most important information is mixed with the old or trivial. In an emergency situation, the central filing system is ignored almost entirely and a crisis team of experts on that particular situation or country is called together to offer its analysis and advice.

The problem of information-flow and use has been long recognized in the foreign-affairs community of our government. Since 1946, some 400 projects and studies in information management have been undertaken, half of them in the State Department and half in the various successor agencies concerned with foreign economic and technical assistance.

The Beginning Steps and Problems

In one informational area of foreign affairs, technological solutions have been vigorously tested—collating information about the State Department's resources. A Foreign Affairs Programming System (FAPS) was established with the objective of bringing together all the strands of U.S. activities and resources abroad, country by country, to give both the Secretary of State and the ambassadors a coherent instrument of command and control. Now elements of the FAPS are being refined to serve the PPBS being introduced.

In 1966, Dr. Charles Hitch, formerly with RAND Corporation and then, as comptroller of the Department of Defense, architect of the programming system introduced by Secretary McNamara, was designated as the chairman of a newly appointed advisory group on foreign-affairs planning-programming-budgeting. This advisory group was charged with developing a PPBS for the State Department. The Stanford Research Institute, State Department personnel, the Bureau of the Budget, and the PPBS personnel of other agencies worked closely with the advisory group. It was expected that, by fiscal 1969, a full PPBS cycle could be developed for Latin America—the first test region. However, this did not happen and it is difficult now to predict when it will. At least one study* has been written on this experience. Basically, it indicates that a lack of top-level involvement and a failure in developing a management strategy for the application of PPBS until now, have been responsible for the faltering of the effort.

Even at the beginning, Richard Barrett, Director of the Office of Management Planning in the State Department, formulated one of the major problems in this way: "Secretary McNamara, in introducing PPBS in the Defense Department, had a definite managerial concept and strategy in mind. State is trying to formulate a managerial strategy at the same time as it is trying to develop a system

---

*F. C. Mosher and J. Harr, untitled study tentatively scheduled for publication under the Inter-University Case Program, Bobbs-Merrill.

to support that strategy." The question is, in the absence of a management strategy, will the computer, now an integral part of the PPBS system, be used merely to decorate and speed up already obsolete processes? Will information technology simply be applied to existing information-gathering processes? Will more information be gathered only to become useless because the persons who need it do not get it, or get it at the wrong time? PPBS, which is principally concerned with planning and budgeting, is only a small part of this dilemma. The problem becomes more complex and urgent, say, in the implementation of policy or crisis management.

Some Pages from Business Experience

But those who plan carefully may be able to learn much from business experience with the application of advanced information technologies. As we have seen in the preceding chapters, the lessons have been learned and still are being learned by business the hard way: mounting costs for useless data, duplication of functions and personnel, large-scale errors in business operations and decisions. The key problem resides in the inability or unwillingness of management to ask itself what it really wants from technology. What kind of information is needed by which persons at what times? What is the relation of the costs of this information to the benefits derived? More and more, such questions are being formulated with insight and imagination and, as a result, the latest technological capabilities have made possible not only a change in the methods but also in the substance of business operations.

For example, certain items can now be mass produced by inserting a magnetic tape into a computer that guides the machine in the manufacturing process. Instead of manufacturing such items at headquarters and shipping them where required, it may be cheaper to ship the magnetic tape and manufacture the items in the market areas. Imaginative thinking through of technology makes entirely new processes and procedures possible.

Banking systems, credit-card companies, and airlines are among the operations whose present scope of service would be impossible without the relatively intelligent use of information technology. One can only imagine the chaos if, for some reason, governmental operations—from traffic control to internal-revenue collection—were to return to the limitations imposed by precomputer administrative and clerical routines.

As we have seen, the complexity of the new technology itself simplifies the relationship between man and machine and makes the machine more and more an integral part of society. The information systems of today already are beginning to provide us with the ability to ask the computer questions through keyboard desk sets, light-pencil drawings on a televisionlike screen, or, to a still limited extent, by voice. Answers to such questions come back through a print-out or on a screen or both. For instance, an engineer can make a sketch with a light pencil on the screen; the computer converts this sketch into a precise engineering draft that appears on the screen and can be rotated in perspective or altered at will. When the engineer gets what he wants, he can have the design either printed out in hard copy or converted to a tape that runs a machine tool, which, in turn, cuts the designed part out of metal. A typical multistation system in a large corporation allows hundreds of managers across the country—and will eventually allow them, across the world—to query a centrally located computer from their desk sets and receive instantaneous replies in visual form.

The key questions that have to be answered in order to build these systems and make them work usefully are: (1) Who needs the information? (2) What kind of information must be made available, in what detail, and how currently? (3) Must the system be complex enough to allow for machine guidance of the questioner, if the question is unclear or unanswerable in the form presented? In other words, what do we want from our technology? As our commercial systems are beginning to demonstrate, we can get what we want.

THE HISTORICAL PROBLEM

The danger that, in the management of foreign affairs, we shall not really demand of the new technologies what they can do resides largely in the long history preceding the introduction of the PPBS concept in government. Just as business, but lagging somewhat behind, the federal government has experimented with and introduced cost-benefit-analyses methods into a growing number of its programs. Just as in business, human, especially managerial, factors tend to perpetuate these methods and to limit severely the potential applications of the new technologies. The technicians are left to fend for themselves, relying on precedent and asking only the questions of the new technologies that could be answered in the absence of those technologies. If this continues, PPBS will remain an accounting tool instead of developing into an instrument for managerial control and policy formulation.

Precedents

A brief review of historical developments in government during the precomputer and early computer eras provides an example approximately analogous to the business problems that are now beginning to be overcome by businesses using intensive analysis and imagination.

1. As early as 1902, cost-benefit analyses for water-resources programs were called for in the Rivers and Harbors Act. And the Flood Control Act of 1936 stated explicitly that projects should only be begun when estimated benefits exceed costs. In 1943, the Bureau of the Budget began to review all such projects on this basis before they were submitted to Congress. Particular guidelines for these reviews were formalized in 1952 and revised in 1961, 1964, and 1965—a period that saw the painful development of methods for business computer applications. Ironically enough, although the most advanced computer and communications technologies were first developed by government for use in defense, space, and related programs from which business was only beginning to learn, little use was made of them in other governmental activities, with the notable exceptions of the Internal Revenue Service, the Bureau of the Census, and the FBI (which have very special histories of their own not relevant to this discussion) and, of course, in payroll and routine accounting.

2. In 1946, another antecedent to PPBS took shape in the Budget Bureau. Longer range projections of up to five years were developed for the preparation and examination of agency budget requests. In 1961, these were readied to prepare public projections of alternative dimension of the

federal budget for the years 1965–70. By 1965, these types of projections were integrated with agency program plans and priorities, more or less containing the elements of the PPBS called for by the Presidential directive of that year, cited at the beginning of this chapter.

3. In 1949, the first Hoover Commission recommended the development of the concept of performance-and-cost-based budgets. The legal framework for this was incorporated in the Budget Accounting and Procedures Act of 1950. A program incorporating the concept actually had begun internally in the Budget Bureau in 1947 and, later, as exercised jointly by the comptroller-general, the Secretary of the Treasury, and the director of the Budget, became known as the Joint Financial Management Improvement Program. It evolved into the present plan for the integrating of planning, programming, budgeting, and accounting.

Thus, we can see that there are in government a number of procedures with a long tradition predating the availability of technologies suitable for the optimum use of information for management-control and policy-planning purposes. Will this tradition and its human carriers delay the development of such optimum use? We have already noted the general business experience in this chapter and have looked at it in detail in the preceding ones. As a whole, it is not encouraging, although significant breakthroughs are now being made after a time lag of more than a decade. The problems of comparing the business experience with the potential of governmental action, especially in the foreign-affairs field, reside in the differences between competitive and noncompetitive environments, the internal complexities and vast responsibilities of government, and the volatility and dangers peculiar to the conduct of foreign policy. These factors could add even greater delays than those experienced by the private sector.

Steps Toward a Solution

However, it is possible that the 1969 moves by the new Administration give promise and could change this prognosis. As mentioned earlier, organizational changes in the State Department are being made—changes directly related to information-flow, analysis, and use. More important appear to be:

- Reorganization of the analytical team around the Secretary, to integrate the work of the former Policy Planning Council (now a planning and coordination staff) with the policy and budgetary planning staffs of the United States Information Agency, the Agency for International Development, the Arms Control and Disarmament Agency, and the Peace Corps
- Reactivation of the Board of the Foreign Service, with Undersecretary Richardson as chairman, to take control of personnel and staffing decisions, not only in the State Department but also in other agencies with overseas operations

In effect, these two moves should reassert the Secretary's managerial control, in terms of the information he receives or designates others to receive, the human factors involved in the flow and analysis of information, and the designation of those responsible for acting upon information.

NEW OPPORTUNITIES IN THE MANAGEMENT OF FOREIGN AFFAIRS

Thus, there appears to be increased recognition that, in the management of foreign affairs, we have new opportunities for the effective use of new technologies, that we have new ways to review what we are doing, as well as what we want to do. This will not only affect who makes the decisions or who is the instrument of response, as in the case of the ambassador, but, for these and even more complex questions, it will also change the nature of the decisions. Further, it will determine whether decisions or conscious responses in particular instances are necessary at all or are built into the system automatically.

The question of what we want raises, as indicated above, numerous questions that must be solved organizationally. Who will make the initial and continuing decisions on the data to be fed into the information system? How is data to be weighted for analysis and summary conclusions? Should more than one system be set up—for example, one for the State Department and one for the Central Intelligence Agency? Who should have access to the information from one or more systems? Should there be a switching center that controls who gets what?

This chapter, however, is not primarily concerned with these organizational questions. The answers to them will depend in large part on how we envisage the total impact of information and communications technologies on the substance of foreign-affairs management. The form we want the conduct of international relations to take—and we still have the weight in the world to shape that, if we assume the leadership—will have a profound effect on what the world looks like. It is these larger questions with which we are attempting to deal here. Several examples come to mind, from past and current experience and from the problems we are likely to face in the future.

A Question from History

When Hitler embarked on the course that led to World War II, beginning with the announcement that Germany would rearm and culminating with the occupations of the Rhineland, Austria, the Sudetenland, and Czechoslovakia, three principal arguments were made by those who counseled against intervention: Hitler could not threaten Europe because Germany did not possess the means for all-out war and, therefore, he should be permitted to assert claims that might be legitimate; Hitler already possessed enough power to make intervention too costly; and Hitler, after he achieved Germany's immediate demands, would live in peace with his neighbors.

The first two arguments were based on inadequate information. The third argument was based on an inadequate appraisal of the man and the psychological forces in Germany supporting him. The proper use of the kind of information and communications technologies now or soon to be available to us could have placed the first two arguments in perspective. Vast quantities of intelligence, most of it not secret but only undigested, on production, manpower, foreign trade, resources, and technological probabilities could have provided the Allies at any stage with an accurate picture of German versus allied capabilities. The imponderables would have remained—questions about who would side with whom, about Hitler the man, and about the psychology of his nation—but even these could have been subjected to analysis aided by information technology. This is not to assert that history would necessarily have been changed; information can still be ignored or misused, and those who make policy are influenced by many factors, some of them essentially irrational. But technology cuts down the area of the unknown, narrows the basis for rational decision.

The Need for Treaties

Many treaties are based on promises to do or not to do things one or the other of the treaty partners cannot know about. This is so especially wtih nonaggression and disarmament treaties and their corollaries. If the ability to collect and process vast quantities of data, ranging from atmospheric samples to economic and transportation statistics, can give any one nation an increasingly accurate picture of trends and unusual activities in other nations, will the universal realization that others can divine a break in faith make such treaties obsolete? This could make the response of one nation to certain actions by others automatic, perhaps preprogrammed through simulation. Such "gaming" on the part of many competing powers could give them such an improved view of the possible consequences of their actions as to save them from many hazardous international experiments. Perhaps, in a crude way, this already is happening. The nuclear-test-ban treaty might be considered just a formalized acknowledgment of mutually perceived facts. Can the use of information systems that are increasingly becoming more responsive and accurate push forward this kind of acknowledgment into broader areas of arms control and, someday, even make certain kinds of treaties obsolete?

Trade Agreements

Both in the negotiation of trade agreements and in their execution, an agreed-upon data base can make almost automatic the evaluation of the impact of concessions and of the responses to the withdrawal or tampering with concessions. Perhaps the principal function of the future trade negotiator will be, first, to arrive at an agreed-upon data base and, second, to negotiate on the basis of his evaluation of the national interest involved in facts known to all. On the other hand, it may be decided that, although this procedure would simplify one part of the negotiations, the facts are of such a proprietary nature as to preclude their use in this manner. In either event, the choice of action will be broadened significantly.

Forecasting

Undoubtedly, information systems for the conduct of foreign affairs will have to include major techniques for the forecasting of technological and socio-economic change. In order to prepare for the consequences of economic development in the emerging nations and in the international exploitation of ocean, subarctic, and extraterrestrial resources, substantial revisions in international law and economic policy obviously are going to be required. Information technology could be applied immediately to the collection of relevant socio-economic data, both on the emerging nations and on newly developing resource areas, and eventually could relate them meaningfully to alternative courses of action—what kinds of investments should be made and by whom, what should be the distribution of costs and benefits, and so on. On this basis of information, the substance of the decisions in these fields could be altered fundamentally. National and international concern could be concentrated on real issues and realistic alternatives.

These are but a few examples of how information and communications technologies could have an impact on the conduct of foreign affairs. The form and substance of what we do in this field are already changing. It is essential that we understand this and act upon the understanding systematically, imaginatively, and with the best techniques available to us.

In the same decades that the new technology has emerged, the number of countries with which the United States conducts relations has more than doubled, the number of departments and agencies involved in foreign affairs has vastly increased, and our sources of information have taken a quantum jump. The very process of decision-making has become infinitely complicated. Under these circumstances, the challenge of conducting our foreign affairs intelligently, of grounding policy on the best possible information, is a challenge to modern management and its use of organizational systems and technological tools.

Is modern management now being applied to the conduct of United States foreign affairs? It appears that a beginning has been made—particularly with the recent moves of the Nixon Administration discussed above. Perhaps in this beginning we may also find that our statesmen —not the technicians, but those who must decide what is to be demanded of the technicians—have begun to think about what they want. For, once again, this is the central question: What do we want from our technology? If we know, we can get it. This is the fact, for both government and business.

Chapter 12

NEW VISTAS IN PUBLIC SERVICE: A CASE STUDY IN URBAN GOVERNMENT

Urban governments offer new markets for business. There are several examples of businesses already working in these areas. The most direct is business participation in setting up and applying systems concepts to the administrative work of urban governments. Next is the business role in applying information technology to analyzing and solving various urban problems, ranging from pollution control to tax collection.

But of even greater potential, and up to now hardly tapped, are fields where business can in effect perform functions now performed by urban governments. One of the most important is education, where the needs have far outgrown the capabilities of traditional methods and of the capacities of existing public school systems.

For urban governments to cope successfully

with the problems of a changing society, the resources available to business will have to be enlisted. Also, it will be necessary to overcome jurisdictional barriers that prevent unified action on matters that know no political barriers. Finally, new ways of determining the priorities set on public services by those who live or work in the cities have to be developed.

Fundamental to the similarities between the problems and opportunities of technological change in the private and public sector are the social changes brought about by the technological innovation.

This chapter is based on an article published in the May, 1967, issue of Governing Urban Society: The Annals of the American Academy of Political and Social Science.

This case study illustrates not only the parallels between the impacts of technological change on government and the private sector but the business opportunities that are growing out of public needs. New markets for business, intimately related to that most fundamentally important business meaning of technological change—the social changes brought about by technological innovations—are developing.

Business, in order to maintain and expand its role in the economy, must take a close look at those markets, at the opportunities that include work in the application of systems technologies and techniques to governmental operations. They are to be found in areas as disparate as education and pollution control, recreation and transportation. There lies the future of economic activity.

Thus, in this case study, more than in any other, the need for business to understand the social forces let loose by technology becomes clear. To initiate the process of gaining such an understanding, it may be useful to consider an apparent paradox.

While technology has greatly broadened the areas of choice and potential action open to the individual, it has also contracted the areas in which individuals and communities can act independently in their own interests. Thus, technology, which is in large part responsible for a widening of opportunities, also blocks the road toward their achievement.

Urban life, itself the result of technological change, especially intensifies the impact of individual action and the need for social control. It is the thesis of this chapter that, in this most important arena of socio-economic action, as in the others presented as case studies, the appropriate application of technology to the roadblocks it itself creates can open the way to the new goals that lie beyond. Involved here are goals related very directly to the quality of life in, for example, education, political action, and the general improvement of the urban environment.

This double nature of technology, as a source and a solution of problems, and our ambivalent attitude toward it have been described by Jacques Barzun in *Science: The Glorious Entertainment:* "From the beginning . . . technological society was greeted with love and hate, despair and hope. Nor was the division only between opposing groups but often within the poet, philosopher, or publicist. The poets particularly were captivated by the Promethean hope of human power overcoming Necessity, even as they protested the spoiling of clear streams and quiet valleys."

This chapter will consider both aspects of technology—its meaning for urban government and for business.

THE CHALLENGES TO URBAN GOVERNMENT

Technological change has fundamentally altered the scope and character of our problems: It has created challenges to urban government in several areas. For example, the need for education at all levels is increasing at an accelerating pace, in terms of quantity and quality. Population growth, the need to provide training and retraining of unskilled labor, and the requirements for the continuing education of even highly skilled persons impose severe burdens on urban school systems.

Urban police, as now equipped and organized, cannot cope with the increasingly intolerable threat of crime.

Traffic congestion, through the failure of urban areas to make rational plans for public transport and traffic flow, threatens to choke commerce and destroy the advantages of proximity. Pollution of air, water, and the countryside cannot be permitted to continue uncontrolled.

The sociological, cultural, and basic welfare effects of unemployment, a traditional urban problem that has been aggravated by technological change, have overwhelmed the means of urban government. Health, cultural, and recreational facilities now provided will have to be expanded to meet the public's expanded expectations and hours of leisure. Cities have frequently been unable to provide a climate that attracts and retains commercial activity.

Furthermore, urban tax systems are ill designed to deal with the accelerated demands created by a technology that is changing the economic structure of cities and their surrounding areas as well as the populations inhabiting them. City property taxes and indirect taxation by states have been inadequate for financing local government services. Their collection is constrained by limitations of residence that have been effectively erased by the socio-economic consequences of technological change. People benefiting from the services of the city have been enabled actually to reside outside the city. Corporate headquarters making use of urban facilities no longer contribute their share to city revenues, since communications and transportation technologies have enabled businesses to move taxable production centers to distant areas.

Technology, however, does not only create these problems. It also provides the means for meeting them and for reaching beyond them to create new areas for individual and communal opportunity. But the effective application of technology is more than the superimposition of modern hardware on old processes. It implies a breakout from the confines of old procedures. The structures that once determined the courses of action taken in accordance with these procedures are no longer necessary or useful. As a matter of fact, they constitute detrimental limitations to the achievement of what is possible. Thus, the solutions to the problems facing urban governments must be sought along other paths.

Systems Analysis for the Examination of Causal Relationships

Urban government faced with the problem of performing a multitude of complex, interrelated, and almost equally important functions, within definite budgetary limitations, can examine, with the aid of systems analysts, the interplay and causal relationships among these functions. The data pertaining to a large number of variables can be brought into play in order to determine priorities for action. The logical and necessary sequence of steps for the achievement of community goals thus can be established, just as for the achievement of business goals discussed earlier in this book.

Systems analysis, properly applied as a technique for the scientific application of information made available through advanced data processing and communications technologies, lends itself to the intelligent establishment and weighting of alternative goals in terms of the resources to be devoted to their attainment. However, organizational and human factors present obstacles to such applications, for the data base supporting systems analysis implies a lessening of the autonomy of various traditional urban departments. There is here also a great similarity to the problems of business organization, where old lines of authority often tend to impede the useful flow of information. In urban governments, the separate data relevant to welfare programs, education projects, and police protection, for example, are often equally relevant to more than one of these. Therefore, not only in the achievement of over-all goals but also in the assembling of data, the close interdependence of various urban functions becomes evident. Actions that do not recognize this interdependence in the most basic areas, such as the building of data bases, are wasteful and even counterproductive.

The widely publicized California experiment in which the state contracted with four aerospace companies to study four major urban problems is a good example of both the value of systems-analysis techniques and the problems involved in its use by civilian agencies. Harold R. Watt of the California Department of Finance commented on both the success and failures of the experiment, and concluded that: "Those . . . who participated in these studies . . . have seen new possibilities in ways of solving the state's problems. The experience has convinced them not only that the techniques of systems analysis are useful but that such an approach may be essential in coping with some of today's and tomorrow's public problems."

Sharing Facilities for Cost Effectiveness

Purchasing or renting from and sharing with private enterprise the information and communications technologies and the systems-analysis techniques already developed by business to meet its own managerial, research, and development needs could provide a cost-effective approach for urban government. Such an approach could make use of various alternatives or combinations of alternatives.

For example, major firms with advanced computer and communications facilities and systems capabilities could be asked to undertake the data-gathering and analytical functions necessary for decision-making by urban governments. In this way, the functions of urban government could concentrate upon making political and value judgments and upon furnishing human service to human beings: police protection and sanitation and individual health care, counseling, and similar programs. Alternatively, urban government may decide to retain a top-level staff of systems-analysts and data-processing managers but rent or purchase hardware, software packages, and services from private enterprise.

Another route, especially for the largest cities, may be the development of total systems capabilities from the most elementary programming through systems design and systems analysis. In that event it may be possible to recoup part of the costs by sharing with or selling to private enterprise the techniques and technologies owned by the city.

A recent variation of these approaches is the establishment of the New York City–RAND Institute. In 1969, some sixteen months after New York City brought in the RAND Corporation to apply systems-analysis techniques to various problems, this nonprofit institute was set up to expand these efforts and put them on a continuing basis. New York City is contributing about $3 million a year, and money is being sought from other sources such as the

Ford Foundation. Among other things, the RAND team has recommended means for increasing police protection during high crime hours and has strengthened the planning, programming, and budgeting systems in several city agencies.

In all these alternatives, recognition must be given to the need for strict legal restraints. Private enterprise must be limited in the way it may use data to which it has access through its work for the city. As discussed in Chapter 9, the nature of the technology itself greatly eases the problem of misuse of information—misuse that threatens privacy or provides unfair competitive advantages. The programs making information available can be so constructed as to answer only specified questions. These answers, in the case of urban government applications, could be limited to receipt by a selected number of politically responsible officials. Thus, for example, the names of individuals with police records or with poor tax and employment histories would never appear before the eyes of unauthorized individuals.

Necessary Jurisdiction Flexibility and Increased Intergovernmental Cooperation

The implications of systems-analysis techniques and information and communications technologies for the internal organization of urban governments are discussed above. The same considerations apply with reference to the relationships between governmental entities in a regional or larger area. Application of systems analysis to the definition and solution of a specific problem of a specific governmental entity illustrates clearly that problems do not fall neatly within politically bounded areas. For example, the waste-management study performed by the Aerojet General Corporation for the state of California concludes that wastes cannot be efficiently managed in the geographic plots dictated by the boundaries of political jurisdiction, but that the geographic boundaries must stem from the analysis of the waste system itself. This is equally true of other problems facing urban government. Furthermore, the difficulties of financing urban governmental services through taxation indicate the need for a redefinition of the relationships between urban governments and those of surrounding areas. The need clearly is for the definition of regional goals and for a flexibility that will enable existing jurisdictions to meet them.

Technology can help here, both in defining goals and in providing the means to meet them. In the case of criminal activity, for example, the mobility of criminals and the widening impact of their actions have made it important to recognize the interdependence of police records and files among cities and regions. Technology is facilitating the response to this situation by large geographic areas. New York State, for example, has created an integrated system of information on crime that makes a central data bank in Albany accessible to various local forces within the state and even in neighboring states. Cooperative systems in New England, Ohio, and California are further examples of this approach.

THE NEW TECHNOLOGICAL CAPABILITIES

It is largely the speed of the new technology that makes possible the manipulation of the complex data needed to support today's informed decisions. This ability was not available before—even if one had been able to pay for it.

And, as discussed in the first chapters of this book, while the speed of calculations and communciations are increasing, the costs of data-processing systems are decreasing. Some of the things that this technology makes possible, in terms of specific urban applications, include:

Econometric or sociometric models that allow for a detailed examination of the interaction of economic and social variables. The public-policy maker can use them, for example, to explore the statistical relationships between the national rate of growth and local unemployment or between juvenile delinquency and school performance.

Input-output models of a region's economy. These can be used to explore the implications of changes in certain industrial sectors of the economy for the industrial base of the region.

Simulation models. Such models can be constructed to provide estimates ranging from optimal traffic flow patterns to cash flows or electric power requirements, and planning can proceed accordingly.

Inadequacies of Present Applications

Nevertheless, in most governmental areas as well as in many of the industries discussed throughout this book, information technology is grossly underutilized. We have largely converted old data collection and control systems to computerized operation rather than designing new systems to utilize the potential of the new technology. Like the early automobile-makers who thought they were making horseless carriages, we are still thinking along the lines of "humanless bookkeeping systems."

According to William H. Mitchel, director of the Municipal Management Information Systems Research Project at the School of Public Administration of the University of California, local governments either have not faced the computer issue or have been content to blunder into the acquisition of hardware with its use dictated by old wives' tales or their commercial equivalent—the advice of vendor salesmen.

Dr. Nachman Bench, when he was consultant to the mayor of New York City, pointed out that, although New York has successfully applied electronic data-processing to traditional operations at an annual cost of $9 million per year, the systems were geared to accounting and tax systems rather than to management decisions. Decentralized operation by departments led to duplication and underutilization, and the analysis of available information was not supported by the methods of systems analysis and operations research. It is hoped that the RAND project mentioned earlier will assist in correcting this wasteful and increasingly dangerous situation.

Government Response

Indeed, governments are beginning to respond to the challenges of modern information technology and systems analysis. Applications that have been proposed or are already in operation include the following:

1. *Central file on individuals.* New Haven, in cooperation with IBM, is developing a complete, computerized, central file of all data on individuals in the city. The file is to be electronically cross-indexed to provide any department with rapid access to information it requires, even though the information may have been generated by a different department.

2. *Information collection and distribution.* In 1965, Lockheed Missiles and Space Corporation prepared for California a statewide information system to provide for a well-organized system of information collection and distribution for all levels of government in the state.

3. *Cooperation in research.* Beginning as far back as 1962, government agencies in five cities (Denver, Wichita, Tulsa, Fort Worth, and Little Rock) were engaged in a pilot program, the Metropolitan Data Center Project, supported by the Federal Urban Renewal Administration. The purpose of the project was the creation of a systems approach to the information needs of various city agencies.

4. *General police communications.* My own firm is working with the City of Phoenix, Arizona, to devise a police network that will speed communications between the man in the field and the computer. Initially, the system may operate with a key-type input device and a voice response, but the possibility of voice input will also be considered.

5. *Specific police files.* New York City maintains a computerized data bank on stolen vehicles and traffic violators. Police hold random checks of vehicles on limited-access thoroughfares by sending the license number of passing vehicles to the computer. In return, they receive information instantaneously identifying stolen vehicles and "scoff-law" violators.

6. *Traffic flow.* Los Angeles, New York, and Toronto are using computers to control traffic lights and traffic flows, and other cities are using computers to simulate optimal traffic flows for control and planning purposes.

7. *Information to local governments.* Edward Kennedy recently introduced a bill to the Senate to make information on all federal programs affecting local governments available to local governments by computer access. This would be of inestimable help to smaller local governments in advising them of the availability of federal funds and assistance. A similar proposal for improving communications at the local level also was made by Dr. Timothy Costello, when he was deputy mayor of New York, for giving neighborhood civic centers access to city hall.

8. *Development of data bases for planning.* The Urban Data Center of the University of Cincinnati has had success in gathering and organizing data on land and structure patterns, social networks, economic systems, and air, water, and ecological systems. This work is the urban planning effort of the city of Cincinnati and is also used by nonprofit planning organizations, commercial operations, and local utilities. Detroit, San Francisco, and Los Angeles are also working with urban data projects.

There are, of course, a large number of examples, some of which have been touched on above, demonstrating how the new technology can be applied to urban problems. Two are expanded on here. One is concrete: the matter of education. The other is conceptual: the evaluation of demands for public services.

INFORMATION AND COMMUNICATIONS TECHNOLOGIES AND EDUCATION

It is statistically evident that educational needs have outgrown our capabilities to meet them in traditional ways. More people need to learn more, and must do so throughout their lives, in order to keep up with the acceleration of changes in working conditions and in the general social environment. Technology is a major cause of these changes and of the new quantitative and qualitative educational needs associated with them.

In the United States, education has been considered a public responsibility from colonial times. However, this responsibility has been met less and less adequately during the past decade, in spite of vastly increased federal and local expenditures. The productivity of the teacher, measured in terms of student learning, is not significantly greater today than it was 100 years ago. As a matter of fact, because of rising salaries and other costs, dollars invested in education have been yielding a decreasing return relative to most other public and private investments.

Thus, we find a growing trend toward reliance on self-education, industrial training, and private schools. But, in our society, this represents only a partial answer. It is an answer from which lessons may be learned, yet in itself it is not adequate to our aspirations.

It seems that private enterprise may lead the way in education. As it does so, however, government should engage it to provide the traditional services of public education. Otherwise we could be threatened by a massive return to education through economic advantage—the stultifying reality of other lands that we have until recently avoided.

Information and communications technologies cannot replace the teacher. But they can improve the teacher's effectiveness in the learning process. A great many experimental programs are under way. While they indicate no possibility of reducing the number of teachers, they do show promise of increasing the productivity of teachers. The key need is for more learning, not for less teaching. Two particular approaches are of particular interest at this stage. The first is computer managed instruction (CMI), a system designed to help the teacher individualize the instructional program. The computer is not involved in the learning process itself, but, in processing and evaluating each student's capabilities, progress, and responses to various types of instruction, it guides the teacher in the use of learning materials and subject matter best suited to the individual student's needs. The second is computer assisted instruction (CAI), an approach that can be applied several ways, ranging from relatively simple drill and practice work to complex interaction between student and computer. The first, of course, implies uses limited to the part of the learning process that requires rote exercise. The second, on the other hand, involves the computer in the presentation of extensive learning materials and in actual dialogue with the student through student use of keyboards, light pencils, and voice for responses and questions. These two approaches, CMI and CAI, are not mutually exclusive and will probably be used in combination with each other and with different types of educational technologies such as television and audiovisual aids.

Robert W. Locke and Daniel Engler of McGraw-Hill predict that, by 1978, some 25 per cent of the schools in the United States will have on-line use of computers for instructional purposes. The important thing to realize, however, is that educational technologies will make education not cheaper but better and more even in quality. For example, my firm has estimated that the nationwide application of advanced educational systems will cost from $5.2 billion to $12.4 billion annually. This represents between 19 per cent and 39 per cent of total current public elementary and secondary school expenditures projected for 1977 by the U.S. Office of Education. Since some 80 per cent of those projected expenditures are for salaries of personnel that the new technologies will not replace, we are quite clearly going to have to raise our educational budgets. Equally clear, however, is the crisis with which education is faced because, even today, with total private and governmental expenditures running at $60 billion or more annually, too few of our children and adults are learning what is necessary and whole segments of our population are falling further and further behind in the competition for economic and social opportunity.

It must be emphasized that educational technologies can be applied only within the context of a major reassessment of educational goals and methods. This fact, of course, is integral to the major theme of this book: Computer and communications technologies, to be used successfully, require fundamental innovations in thought and action by the user. But in education, as in other areas, the dividends on the investment in planning can be enormous. An indication of these dividends is given by the results of an experiment, using control groups, conducted by International Business Machines and involving courses on data processing. The use of CAI resulted in a 5 per cent increase of student comprehension and a 25 per cent decrease in learning time, as compared to the conventionally trained control groups.

Thus, education is a primary public concern, especially acute in urban settings, where the thoughtful application of technology can contribute to the solution of problems technological change has itself in large part caused. To do so will require money and time, but the need is uncontrovertible.

EVALUATING PUBLIC DEMAND FOR PUBLIC SERVICES

Another area that requires the attention of urban governments is the collection of information regarding the value placed by citizens on government services and the use of such information as a guide in establishing levels of expenditure. In this regard it is important to note that one of the significant differences between private goods and public services is the way in which demand for them is expressed and the way in which the goods are furnished. If there is an increased demand for hot-water bottles or haircuts, the consumers go to the respective establishments where these commodities are sold. Increased demand may send prices up, in the short run, until the producers in these industries expand their capacity by drawing in additional capital and labor. It is not so with mass-transit systems, public education, or police services. If there is insufficient public provision of these services relative to the demand, they become overcrowded, and the public suffers loss of real income from not being able to purchase the services they desire. The costs are borne in terms of congestion and discomfort, second-rate education, rising insurance premiums, and fear for one's personal safety. Citizens are supposed to be able to remedy the situation at the polls, but the choices are often not presented there in any clear-cut way, and for urban areas there are problems of overlapping jurisdictions and lack of financial sovereignty. Many citizens have sought private sources for education, protection, and transportation; others, have moved to other communities. Their support is thus lost for the improvement of public services in the deficient community.

Perhaps the most difficult problem of all is the lack of a conceptual framework to compare the benefits of public services with costs—the very root of the economic rationale for public administration of "collective" goods. Public officials find it difficult to compare the utility to the people of an extra dollar's worth of private consumption with the loss of a dollar's worth of public services in the form of parks or snow removal. And the people, individually and in groups, are also undecided on their real needs and what they are willing to pay in order to meet them.

The revolution in information and market research techniques makes possible some systematic improvements in the knowledge that could be obtained about the people's valuation of the relative importance of public services. Perhaps, equally important, it also enables the people to determine what they want and are ready to pay. No large private corporation today would launch a new product for the consumer without engaging in market research to determine the extent of the available market. Surely it is possible to use similar methods to ascertain preferences and quantitative judgments as to the relative importance of people's demands for public goods.

Several years ago, the state of Washington conducted a survey to determine the recreational value of the state's salmon fishery to evaluate proposed expenditures on hatcheries, pollution control, and fish ladders. A sample questionnaire was distributed to fishermen, asking them to list their expenditures for various items connected with the sport and asking them how much they would be willing to pay for a fishing license if it were required. The information collected helped to establish an estimate of the recreational value of the sport to the state and to the fishermen of the state.

Public planners need to know how much air pollution is costing the people in terms of actual cleaning and redecorating costs. The costs in discomfort could be estimated by asking people how much they would be willing to pay to breathe clean air. Such estimates of the public losses from air pollution in actual costs and in pleasure foregone can be used in the context of a systems analysis approach that depends heavily on quantifiable objectives. Urban areas could get sophisticated estimates of the costs of crime, pollution, and congestion. They could obtain estimates of the value placed by people on good schools, parks, libraries, and cultural facilities to guide them in expenditures.

In effect, the development of these kinds of estimates would serve the double purpose of informing both the urban governments and the public. The latter may be of special significance because individuals and special-interest groups would be able to view their own priorities in the light of those of their fellow citizens. Thus, the information gathered could have profound consequences in terms of the substantive issues decided through the political process. The citizenry would be able to discern what it wants and judge political actions in this context. Of course, as in the business and foreign affairs case studies discussed in this book, the fundamental problem is to ask the right questions of the new technology.

Technological change affects the functions of government by changing the character and quality of public services that are needed by the public and by changing the costs or providing and not providing those services. The growth in the size and range of functions of governmental units in the United States over the past century has not resulted from some Parkinsonian tendency of bureaucrats to reproduce their numbers at a geometric rate. It has occurred because of the public's recognition that the development of an urban, industrial society poses a need for social control of the environment that is different from the need of a sparsely settled, agricultural society. It has come about because of an increasing realization that governments can play a valuable role in the positive provision of health, transportation, education, leisure-time facilities, and amenities for improving the quality of life, as well as the traditional functions of providing for security of person and property and a stable social framework.

The important question facing urban governments is not whether they will provide services at a rising level but at what rate the provision of public services will increase. This is a quantitative decision. It is one that ought to be based on hard facts about people's preferences and the social returns from alternative expenditures. It is also a decision that will depend in large part on the cost effectiveness of government-administered programs. Finally, it is a decision that must take into account the increasing potential for private-sector contributions to the substantial and managerial needs of government services.

New managerial concepts will inevitably be applied to the evaluation of local government operations as well as to the operations themselves. The communities that offer low-quality services to their citizens at high costs will be exposed to the scrutiny of public opinion and, perhaps, federal intervention. Local governments might not be open to the same sanctions as private corporations for failure to operate efficiently, but the men who function as their managers and boards of directors will find their tenure in office as uncomfortable as their counterparts in the private sector of the economy if they fail to use the resources of modern technology to serve the public.

Technology has been the cause of many urban problems. But technology can also contribute in many areas to solutions. A clear definition of goals, the establishment of a solid conceptual framework for viewing those goals—one independent of fragmented political jurisdictions and concentration on short-term costs and benefits—is basic. Technology, and the techniques associated with it, can help build this framework, which, once established, will enable governments to use technology to improve services in all traditional areas and to provide new services in their attempts to do the things that Abraham Lincoln suggested, more than a century ago, were their proper function: "to do those things for the people which they cannot do as well or as cheaply for themselves."

THE CHANGING ROLE OF THE COMPUTER

Management application

1965

In the two-decade span from 1965 to 1985, computer systems applications will evolve from the unrelated elementary uses which were typical of the 1950's and early 1960's to the highly integrated and interdependent systems projected for 1985. In this first time frame, computers are doing essentially what clerks had done before, only doing it electronically. The value of the computers, when it was measured at all, was calculated by the rather primitive methods of cost displacement of clerical and machine resources.

1968

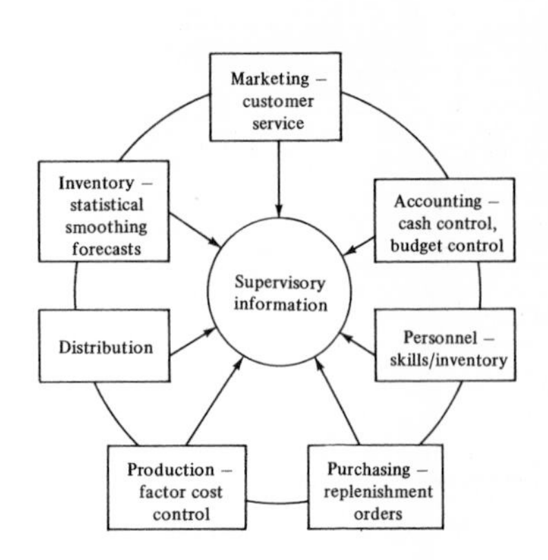

In this second time frame, roughly the present, the computer is beginning to effect change not only in how a business operates but in what it does. Supervisory management is undergoing transformation in all the basic areas of corporate activity. Measurement by cost displacement has already become obsolescent.

Criteria used in evaluation

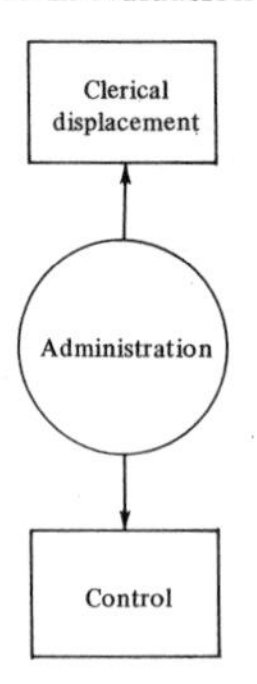

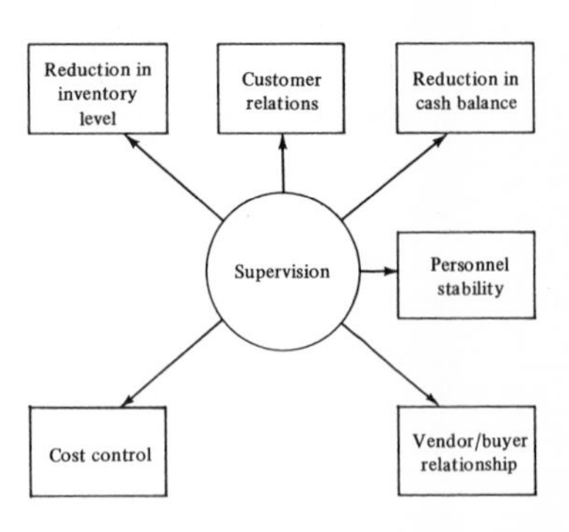